Grade **3**

P9-BJE-342

DAILY LANGUAGE PRACTICE

by Sandy Pobst

Daily Language Practice provides a structured approach to building and reviewing your students' language and literacy skills. Each of the 36 weeks includes daily, weekly, and monthly activities.

Weekly Skill
Practice one skill each week

Monthly Review
Apply skills learned each month

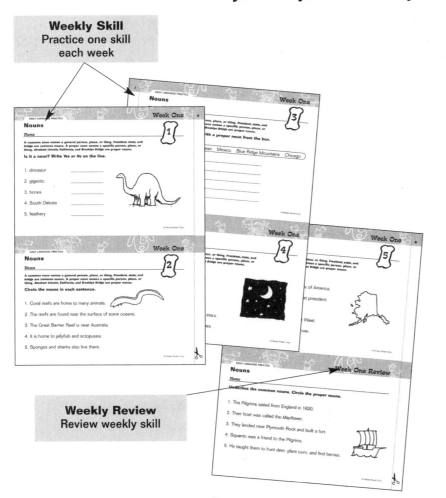

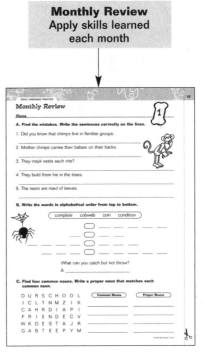

Weekly Review
Review weekly skill

Table of Contents

Skills: Scope and Sequence

The Scope and Sequence chart on this page provides a complete overview of the skills reviewed in this book. Use this chart to select practice activities that cover skills you are currently teaching or to review previously taught skills.

Skill	1	2	3	4	5	6	7	8	9	10	11	12	13	14	15	16	17	18	19	20	21	22	23	24	25	26	27	28	29	30	31	32	33	34	35	36
Punctuation and Capitalization																																				
End Punctuation	X																																			
Capitalizing Proper Nouns				X																																
Commas in Dates and Addresses						X																														
Commas in a Series									X																											
Commas in Dialogue & Direct Address																													X							
Quotation Marks																										X										
Capitalizing Titles																														X						
Grammar																																				
Nouns	X																																			
Plural Nouns					X																															
Verbs			X																																	
Contractions								X																												
Subject-Verb Agreement													X																							
Verb Forms										X					X																					
Adjectives																X																				
Possessive Nouns																	X																			
Adverbs																			X																	
Types of Sentences		X																																		
Complete Sentences and Fragments																				X																
Compound Sentences																																X				
Run-On Sentences																																	X			
Pronouns																						X														
Comparatives and Superlatives																								X												
Usage Review																																				X
Vocabulary																																				
Synonyms							X																													
Antonyms														X																						
Prefixes																							X													
Suffixes																																		X		
Reading and Research																																				
Alphabetical Order		X																																		
Fact and Opinion													X																							
Homophones																											X									
Interpreting Graphic Sources of Info																												X								
Using Parts of a Book																															X					
Spelling																																				
Spelling (Long Vowel Sounds)			X																																	
Spelling (Initial and Final Blends)										X																										
Spelling (Inflected Endings)																		X																		
Spelling (Commonly Misspelled Words)																																	X			

Using This Book

Daily Practice

This reproducible book provides daily language practice with many essential third-grade language arts skills. You can use these quick activities in a variety of classroom situations—as daily warm-ups, quick assessment tools, or helpful reviews.

The book's organization features 36 weekly practice sessions centered around a single topic, followed by a monthly review of the skills covered during the previous four weeks. This approach allows for in-depth and focused practice of essential language arts concepts in a concentrated time frame. Whenever appropriate, the exercises use material from *Weekly Reader®* magazine. This engaging resource provides high-interest content and skill practice in context.

The exercises offered for the first part of each week are simpler. These afford students the opportunity to experience success while practicing previously introduced skills. As the week progresses, the activities gradually become more challenging. Likewise, the more complex skills are offered as the year progresses.

When planning your daily routine, try one or more of these management techniques:

- Distribute copies of each daily page to individual students or to small groups. You might choose to have students work together for Day One through Day Three and then individually for Days Four and Five. When students work independently, encourage them to exchange work with a partner and compare and discuss their answers. Or, review the correct responses together as a large group.

- Use an overhead projector or create transparencies to complete the work in a large group. Ask volunteers to help complete each item. Try completing Day One as a whole-class activity to review the week's skill. Then have students work independently or in pairs throughout the week.

- Direct students to complete the activity pages for homework. Encourage students to discuss their work with their families.

Weekly Reviews

There is a weekly review to reinforce the work of the previous days. Many of the weekly reviews use a "Find the Mistakes" format that allows students to practice identifying errors in context. You can use this review as an assessment, collecting and scoring each student's work individually. You might prefer to use this skills review as an assessment tool to determine weak areas or gaps in your students' knowledge.

Monthly Reviews

At the end of each four-week set, there is an activity page that reviews the skills taught during that month. Each monthly review includes a "Find the Mistakes" activity or a fun word game.

Skills Overview

The Scope and Sequence chart on the previous page provides a complete overview of the skills reviewed in this book. Use this chart to select practice activities that cover skills you are currently teaching or to review previously taught skills.

Nouns

1

Name _____

A common noun names a general person, place, or thing. *President, state,* and *bridge* are common nouns. A proper noun names a specific person, place, or thing. *Abraham Lincoln, California,* and *Brooklyn Bridge* are proper nouns.

Is it a noun? Write *Yes* or *No* on the line.

1. dinosaur _____

2. gigantic _____

3. bones _____

4. South Dakota _____

5. feathery _____

© Weekly Reader Corp.

Nouns

2

Name _____

A common noun names a general person, place, or thing. *President, state,* and *bridge* are common nouns. A proper noun names a specific person, place, or thing. *Abraham Lincoln, California,* and *Brooklyn Bridge* are proper nouns.

Circle the nouns in each sentence.

1. Coral reefs are home to many animals.

2. The reefs are found near the surface of some oceans.

3. The Great Barrier Reef is near Australia.

4. It is home to jellyfish and octopuses.

5. Sponges and sharks also live there.

© Weekly Reader Corp.

Nouns

Name _____

3

A common noun names a general person, place, or thing. *President, state,* and *bridge* are common nouns. A proper noun names a specific person, place, or thing. *Abraham Lincoln, California,* and *Brooklyn Bridge* are proper nouns.

Match each common noun with a proper noun from the box. Write it on the correct line.

| Mojave Desert   Indian Ocean   Mexico   Blue Ridge Mountains   Chicago |

1. country _____

2. desert _____

3. city _____

4. ocean _____

5. mountain _____

Nouns

Name _____

4

A common noun names a general person, place, or thing. *President, state,* and *bridge* are common nouns. A proper noun names a specific person, place, or thing. *Abraham Lincoln, California,* and *Brooklyn Bridge* are proper nouns.

Underline the common nouns.

1. Our sun is a star.

2. Stars are made of hot gases.

3. Planets move around the sun.

4. Some scientists study planets and stars.

5. They use special tools like telescopes.

Nouns

Name _____

A common noun names a general person, place, or thing. *President*, *state*, and *bridge* are common nouns. A proper noun names a specific person, place, or thing. *Abraham Lincoln*, *California*, and *Brooklyn Bridge* are proper nouns.

Circle the proper nouns.

1. Our country is the United States of America.

2. George Washington was the first president.

3. Alaska is the largest state.

4. The Rocky Mountains are in the West.

5. The Mississippi River is a long river.

Nouns

Name _____

Underline the common nouns. Circle the proper nouns.

1. The Pilgrims sailed from England in 1620.

2. Their boat was called the *Mayflower*.

3. They landed near Plymouth Rock and built a fort.

4. Squanto was a friend to the Pilgrims.

5. He taught them to hunt deer, plant corn, and find berries.

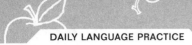

End Punctuation

Name _____

A statement is a sentence that tells something. A question is a sentence that asks something. An exclamation is a sentence that shows extreme emotion.

**What type of sentence is it? Write *S* if it is a statement.
Write *Q* if it is a question. Write *E* if it is an exclamation.**

1. _____ Don't share those germs!

2. _____ Coughing and sneezing can spread germs.

3. _____ Do you cover your mouth when you sneeze?

4. _____ Why is it important to wash your hands?

5. _____ Germs that make people sick can be on your hands.

End Punctuation

Name _____

A statement is a sentence that tells something. A question is a sentence that asks something. An exclamation is a sentence that shows extreme emotion.

**What type of sentence is it? Write *S* if it is a statement.
Write *Q* if it is a question. Write *E* if it is an exclamation.**

1. _____ Can you name some dinosaurs?

2. _____ Dinosaurs lived millions of years ago.

3. _____ Some dinosaurs ate plants.

4. _____ Do you know what the meat-eaters are called?

5. _____ What interesting animals!

End Punctuation

Name _____

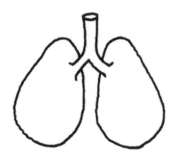

Use a period (.) at the end of a statement. Use a question mark (?) at the end of a sentence that asks something. Use an exclamation point (!) at the end of a sentence to show extreme emotion.

Add the correct end punctuation. Write a period, question mark, or exclamation point on the line.

1. Do you know what your lungs do _____

2. They help you breathe air _____

3. Why do your lungs need clean air _____

4. Clean air keeps your lungs healthy _____

5. Lungs are great _____

End Punctuation

Name _____

Use a period (.) at the end of a statement. Use a question mark (?) at the end of a sentence that asks something. Use an exclamation point (!) at the end of a sentence to show extreme emotion.

These sentences end with an incorrect punctuation mark. Write each sentence correctly on the line.

1. Have you ever looked at the night sky.

_____

2. What a lot of stars?

_____

3. They are part of our galaxy?

_____

4. Do you know what a galaxy is!

_____

5. A galaxy is an island of stars!

_____

End Punctuation

Name _____

Use a period (.) at the end of a statement. Use a question mark (?) at the end of a sentence that asks something. Use an exclamation point (!) at the end of a sentence to show extreme emotion.

Circle the correct end punctuation.

1. Wow, it's cold outside   .   ?   !

2. Some animals hibernate in cold weather   .   ?   !

3. Can you name some animals that hibernate .   ?   !

4. Frogs hibernate in the mud   .   ?   !

5. Would you like to hibernate   .   ?   !

End Punctuation

Name _____

Write each sentence correctly on the line.

1. Do you take care of your lungs.

_____

2. Exercise makes your lungs strong?

_____

3. Doctors make sure your lungs are healthy

_____

4. Did you know that smoking can harm your lungs!

_____

5. You should never smoke?

Alphabetical Order

Name _____

Alphabetical order is the same as ABC order. In an alphabetical list, words that begin with *a* come before words that begin with *b,* and so on. If two words begin with the same first letter, look at the second letter of each word.

Write the words in alphabetical order.

| reptile   animal   mammal   amphibian   bird   fish |

1. _____

2. _____

3. _____

4. _____

5. _____

6. _____

Alphabetical Order

Name _____

Alphabetical order is the same as ABC order. In an alphabetical list, words that begin with *a* come before words that begin with *b,* and so on. If two words begin with the same first letter, look at the second letter of each word.

Are the words in alphabetical order? Write *Yes* or *No.*

1. apple   avocado   banana   _____

2. bobcat   bear   bird   _____

3. oak   pine   maple   _____

4. math   reading   writing   _____

5. port   ship   sailor   _____

Alphabetical Order

Name _____

Alphabetical order is the same as ABC order. In an alphabetical list, words that begin with *a* come before words that begin with *b,* and so on. If two words begin with the same first letter, look at the second letter of each word.

Circle the words that belong between the guide words *ocean* and *oval* in a dictionary.

1.	oak	other
2.	occur	onion
3.	onward	ox
4.	ounce	oven
5.	obey	ostrich

Alphabetical Order

Name _____

Alphabetical order is the same as ABC order. In an alphabetical list, words that begin with *a* come before words that begin with *b,* and so on. If two words begin with the same first letter, look at the second letter of each word.

Write the words in alphabetical order.

foot   arm   elbow   ankle   face

1. _____

2. _____

3. _____

4. _____

5. _____

Alphabetical Order

Name _____

Alphabetical order is the same as ABC order. In an alphabetical list, words that begin with *a* come before words that begin with *b,* and so on. If two words begin with the same first letter, look at the second letter of each word.

Circle the words that belong between the guide words *carefree* and *compare* in a dictionary.

1.   calm   cobweb

2.   castle   concern

3.   cattle   court

4.   cane   coin

5.   capital   catnip

Alphabetical Order

Name _____

Write these words in alphabetical order.

1. Asia, Africa, America, Antarctica

_____

2. duckling, cub, piglet, calf

_____

3. rose, zinnia, daisy, lily

_____

4. pencil, paper, pen, pad

_____

5. rooster, raven, robin, sparrow

_____

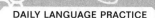

Spelling (Long Vowel Sounds)

3

Name _____

The long *i* sound can be spelled in many ways.

Read each clue. Then circle the correctly spelled answer.

1.	It belongs to me	mi	migh	my
2.	Something that is seen	sight	sit	syte
3.	To move through the air	fligh	fly	fli
4.	Not the truth	lie	ligh	leye
5.	To discover	fined	fighnd	find

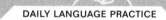

Spelling (Long Vowel Sounds)

4

Name _____

The long *o* sound can be spelled in many ways.

Circle each word that is NOT spelled correctly.
Write the correct spelling on the line.

1. We have won moast of the games we've
   played this year.   _____

2. Our coche is very proud of us.   _____

3. Not long agoe, we had trouble playing
   as a team.   _____

4. Some of the players spoak up.   _____

5. Now we may win the goald medal!   _____

Spelling (Long Vowel Sounds)

1

Name _____

The long *a* sound can be spelled in many ways.

Circle the correct spelling in each line.

1.   raise   rase

2.   neighbor   nieghbor

3.   trayl   trail

4.   craon   crayon

5.   weigh   wiegh

Spelling (Long Vowel Sounds)

2

Name _____

The long *e* sound can be spelled in many ways.

Write the correctly spelled word on the line.

1. Last night we went to the _____ store.
(videeo, video)

2. The store was _____.
(busea, busy)

3. We couldn't find _____ movies we wanted to see.
(any, anee)

4. The clerk said a _____ had stolen most of the movies.
(theef, thief)

5. No one had any _____ who had done it.
(idea, ideea)

Spelling (Long Vowel Sounds)

5

Name _____

The long *u* sound can be spelled in many ways.

Circle the correct spelling in each line.

1.   goose   gews

2.   croo   crew

3.   jooce   juice

4.   broom   brewm

5.   soop   soup

Spelling (Long Vowel Sounds)

Name _____

Find the mistakes. Write each sentence correctly on the line.

1. The island's warm breazes bloo gently through the treas.

_____

2. I waved helloe to my friends as I walked past.

_____

3. Fresh froot was piled hi in the market.

_____

4. I picked out mangos and gave them to the woman to way.

_____

5. Then I added them to mie loade.

_____

Monthly Review

Name _____

A. Find the mistakes. Write the sentences correctly on the lines.

1. Did you know that chimps live in familee groups.

_____

2. Mother chimps carree their babies on their backs.

_____

3. They mayk nests eech nite?

_____

4. They build them hie in the trees.

_____

5. The nests are maid of leeves.

_____

B. Write the words in alphabetical order from top to bottom.

(complete   cobweb   coin   condition)

◯ _ _ _ _ _ _ _

_ _ ◯ _ _ _ _

_ _ _ _ _ ◯ _ _ _ _

_ _ _ _ _ ◯ _ _ _ _

What can you catch but not throw?

A _____

C. Find four common nouns. Look across and down. Write a proper noun that matches each common noun.

D	U	R	S	C	H	O	O	L
I	C	L	T	N	M	Z	I	K
C	A	H	R	D	I	A	P	I
F	R	I	E	N	D	E	C	V
W	K	O	E	S	T	A	J	R
G	A	B	T	E	E	P	Y	M

(**Common Nouns**)   (**Proper Nouns**)

_____   _____

_____   _____

_____   _____

_____   _____

Verbs

Name _____

A verb is a word that describes an action. *Run, jump,* and *fly* are verbs. Some verbs, such as *think, dream,* and *discover,* name mental actions.

Is the word a verb? Write *Yes* or *No.*

_____ 1. black

_____ 2. carry

_____ 3. baseball

_____ 4. sleep

_____ 5. educate

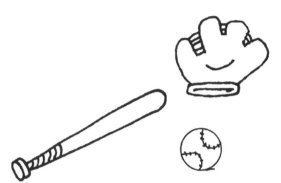

Verbs

Name _____

A verb is a word that describes an action. *Run, jump,* and *fly* are verbs. Some verbs, such as *think, dream,* and *discover,* name mental actions.

Circle the verbs in each sentence.

1. Dr. Jane Goodall studied chimpanzees.

2. She lived with them in Africa.

3. Dr. Goodall learned a lot about the chimps.

4. Chimpanzees often stay in large groups.

5. They use tools to gather food.

Verbs

Name _____

A verb is a word that describes an action. *Run, jump,* and *fly* are verbs. Some verbs, such as *think, dream,* and *discover,* name mental actions.

Circle the verbs.

1. spaceship   float

2. protect   helmet

3. spill   food

4. muscles   suggest

5. improve   circus

© Weekly Reader Corp.

Verbs

Name _____

A verb is a word that describes an action. *Run, jump,* and *fly* are verbs. Some verbs, such as *think, dream,* and *discover,* name mental actions.

Circle the verb in each sentence.

1. Some holidays make winter bright.

2. Many African Americans celebrate Kwanzaa.

3. Some people decorate trees for Christmas.

4. Jewish people observe Hanukkah for eight nights.

5. Some families eat special foods at the end of Ramadan.

© Weekly Reader Corp.

Verbs

Name _____

A verb is a word that describes an action. *Run, jump,* and *fly* are verbs. Some verbs, such as *think, dream,* and *discover,* name mental actions.

Write a verb on the line to complete each sentence.

1. Doctors _____ sick people.

2. Doctors _____ special tools.

3. They _____ your heart and lungs.

4. They _____ in your ears.

5. Doctors _____ special people!

Verbs

Name _____

Circle the verbs in each sentence.

1. Bald eagles live in almost every state in America.

2. They lay eggs from November to January.

3. The eggs hatch after 35 days.

4. The young eagles fly about three months later.

5. Thousands of eagles gather in Alaska to catch salmon.

DAILY LANGUAGE PRACTICE

Capitalization

1

Name _____

Proper nouns name a specific person, place, or thing. They begin with capital letters. *Abraham Lincoln, California,* and *Brooklyn Bridge* are proper nouns. Capitalize each word in the proper noun, as in *North Carolina* and *Empire State Building.*

Circle the correct word or phrase.

1. Davis elementary School   Davis Elementary School

2. Grand Canyon   Grand canyon

3. Running Fox Trail   Running fox Trail

4. mount Hood   Mount Hood

5. Alexander Graham Bell   Alexander graham bell

DAILY LANGUAGE PRACTICE

Capitalization

2

Name _____

Proper nouns name a specific person, place, or thing. They begin with capital letters. *Abraham Lincoln, California,* and *Brooklyn Bridge* are proper nouns. Capitalize each word in the proper noun, as in *North Carolina* and *Empire State Building.*

Underline the proper nouns that need capital letters. Write the words correctly on the line.

1. The rocky mountains are in the United States. _____

2. They stretch from New Mexico to canada.   _____

3. Many people visit pikes peak.   _____

4. It was named for zebulon pike.   _____

5. The first woman to climb the mountain
   was Julia holmes.   _____

Capitalization

3

Name _____

Proper nouns name a specific person, place, or thing. They begin with capital letters. *Abraham Lincoln, California,* and *Brooklyn Bridge* are proper nouns. Capitalize each word in the proper noun, as in *North Carolina* and *Empire State Building.*

These proper nouns are missing capital letters. Write each correctly on the line.

1. New york City _____

2. lake Superior _____

3. Pacific ocean _____

4. golden gate Bridge _____

5. Colorado river _____

Capitalization

4

Name _____

Proper nouns name a specific person, place, or thing. They begin with capital letters. *Abraham Lincoln, California,* and *Brooklyn Bridge* are proper nouns. Capitalize each word in the proper noun, as in *North Carolina* and *Empire State Building.*

Find the proper nouns that need capital letters. Write each sentence correctly on the line.

1. George washington carver was a great american.

_____

2. He was born near diamond grove, Missouri.

_____

3. Later, Carver taught at the tuskegee Institute.

_____

4. He invented peanut butter while he was working in alabama.

_____

5. The George Washington Carver national monument honors his memory.

_____

Capitalization

5

Name _____

Proper nouns name a specific person, place, or thing. They begin with capital letters. *Abraham Lincoln, California,* and *Brooklyn Bridge* are proper nouns. Capitalize each word in the proper noun, as in *North Carolina* and *Empire State Building.*

**Underline the proper nouns that need capital letters.
Write the words correctly on the line.**

1. Much of the mojave desert is in California.
   _____

2. death valley lies near the Mojave.
   _____

3. It is the hottest place in america.
   _____

4. One july, the temperature hit 134 degrees.
   _____

5. No wonder towns like Chloride city are now ghost towns!
   _____

Capitalization

Name _____

Write each sentence correctly on the line.

1. The ocean didn't scare amelia earhart.
   _____

2. She flew across the atlantic ocean by herself.
   _____

3. She also flew from honolulu to california.
   _____

4. In 1937, earhart started to fly around the world.
   _____

5. Her plane disappeared near howland island in the pacific ocean.
   _____

Plural Nouns

Name _____

1

A plural noun names more than one.
Add –s to a singular noun to form most plurals.

Write the plural to complete each sentence.

1. The American flag has 50 _____.
   (star)

2. Each star stands for one of the _____.
   (state)

3. The 13 _____ stand for the original colonies.
   (stripe)

4. Some people use red, white, and blue _____ to make a flag design.
   (sticker)

5. They sing the _____ to "The Star-Spangled Banner."
   (word)

Plural Nouns

2

Name _____

Add –es to form the plural for most nouns that end in *s*, *x*, *ch*, or *sh*.

Write the plural of each noun.

1. fox _____

2. beach _____

3. class _____

4. brush _____

5. inch _____

Plural Nouns

3

Name _____

For most nouns that end in *y*, change the *y* to *i* and add –es to form the plural.

Write the plural noun to complete each sentence.

1. Four _____ ago, people from Europe began settling in America.
   (century)

2. Many people were looking for_____.
   (opportunity)

3. They moved into new _____.
   (territory)

4. They built small _____.
   (community)

5. Some of these grew into large _____.
   (city)

Plural Nouns

4

Name _____

Some nouns have irregular plural forms.

Write the plural of each noun on the line.

1. tooth _____

2. man _____

3. goose _____

4. child _____

5. woman _____

DAILY LANGUAGE PRACTICE

Plural Nouns

5

Name _____

Add –s or –es to form most plural nouns. Some nouns have irregular plural forms.

Circle the incorrect plural. Write the correct word on the line.

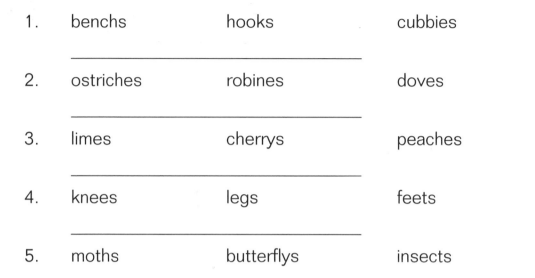

1.　benchs　　　hooks　　　　cubbies

　　_____

2.　ostriches　　robines　　　doves

　　_____

3.　limes　　　　cherrys　　　peaches

　　_____

4.　knees　　　　legs　　　　　feets

　　_____

5.　moths　　　　butterflys　　insects

　　_____

© Weekly Reader Corp.

Week Seven Review

DAILY LANGUAGE PRACTICE

Plural Nouns

Name _____

Find the mistakes. Write each sentence correctly on the line.

1. Librarys are like treasure chests.

_____

2. They have bookes that are full of adventures.

_____

3. Climb the world's tallest mountaines with Reinhold Messner.

_____

4. Push your way through the branchs and vines of the Amazon.

_____

5. What richs will you find in your library?

_____

© Weekly Reader Corp.

Synonyms

1

Name

Synonyms are words that have similar meanings.

Are these words synonyms? Write *Yes* or *No* on the line.

_____	1. ill	sick
_____	2. happy	gloomy
_____	3. hard	difficult
_____	4. leap	jump
_____	5. quick	slow

Synonyms

2

Name

Synonyms are words that have similar meanings.

Write the letter of the word that has a similar meaning on the line.

_____	1. automobile	a. street
_____	2. ocean	b. boat
_____	3. ship	c. jet
_____	4. road	d. car
_____	5. airplane	e. sea

Synonyms

3

Name _____

Synonyms are words that have similar meanings.

Circle the synonyms in each line.

1.   reader   author   writer

2.   calm   moody   peaceful

3.   correct   right   wrong

4.   eyes   glance   look

5.   smell   sight   odor

Synonyms

4

Name _____

Synonyms are words that have similar meanings.

Find a word that has the same meaning as the word in *italics*. Write the synonym on the line.

1. We have a _____ in our classroom today.
   guest

2. She seems very _____.
   nice

3. I have an important _____ to complete.
   job

4. We want to find out if this rock is _____.
   empty

5. I need to _____ everyone's actions.
   watch

hollow

task

visitor

pleasant

observe

DAILY LANGUAGE PRACTICE

Synonyms

Name _____

Synonyms are words that have similar meanings.

Circle the synonyms in each line.

1. terrified   scared   dark

2. sunshine   gloom   darkness

3. begin   first   start

4. autumn   fall   spring

5. brave   weak   heroic

DAILY LANGUAGE PRACTICE

Week Eight Review

Synonyms

Name _____

Find a word that has the same meaning as the word in *italics*. Write the synonym on the line.

1. Most dinosaurs were _____ animals.
   big

2. Some dinosaurs were _____.
   little

3. Some, like T. rex, were very _____.
   scary

4. The biggest dinosaurs were not very _____.
   fast

5. Do you think dinosaurs had _____ roars?
   loud

tiny

huge

speedy

noisy

frightening

Monthly Review

Name _____

A. Find the mistakes. Write each sentence correctly on the line.

1. Some early americans led exciting lifes.

_____

2. Paul revere rode to lexington, massachusetts, at midnight.

_____

3. The british soldieres were on their way to arrest samuel adams.

_____

4. paul revere warned everyone along the way.

_____

5. Soon, the Minutemans were ready to fight for freedom.

_____

B. Find five verbs. Look across and down. Write them on the lines.

```
B  R  I  N  G  S
I  A  J  S  B  C
E  C  P  A  U  R
R  E  U  F  K  A
Q  L  I  F  T  T
U  S  M  D  O  C
L  M  A  R  C  H
```

_____

_____

_____

_____

_____

C. Complete the puzzle. Each answer is a synonym for the clue.

Across
3. Powerful
4. Sad
6. Stare
7. Shout

Down
1. Discovered
2. Little
5. Tugs

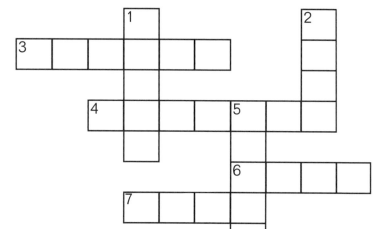

Commas

Name _____

Use a comma between a date and a year, as in *June 16, 2006*.

Each date is missing a comma. Write each date correctly on the line.

1. June 2 1933   _____

2. December 5 1957   _____

3. March 22 2006   _____

4. September 23 1999   _____

5. April 12 2001   _____

Commas

Name _____

Use a comma between the name of a city and state, as in *Columbus, Ohio*.

Each address is missing a comma. Write each address correctly on the line.

1. Denver Colorado   _____

2. Atlanta Georgia   _____

3. Topeka Kansas   _____

4. Hartford Connecticut   _____

5. Madison Wisconsin   _____

Commas

Name _____

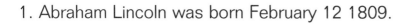

Use a comma between a date and a year. *Sara's birthday is March 4, 2000.* Use a comma between the name of a city and state, as in *Columbus, Ohio.*

Each sentence is missing a comma. Write a comma in the correct place.

1. Abraham Lincoln was born February 12 1809.

2. He was born in Hodgenville Kentucky.

3. Lincoln moved to New Salem Illinois.

4. He was elected president on November 6 1860.

5. President Lincoln freed the slaves in the South on January 1 1863.

Commas

Name _____

Use a comma between a date and a year. *Sara's birthday is March 4, 2000.* Use a comma between the name of a city and state, as in *Columbus, Ohio.*

Each sentence is missing a comma. Write each sentence correctly on the line.

1. The world's largest watermelon was grown in Hope Arkansas.

   _____

2. It weighed almost 270 pounds (123 kg) on September 3 2005.

   _____

3. The world's heaviest tomato grew in Edmond Oklahoma.

   _____

4. A 19-pound (9 kg) carrot was grown in Palmer Alaska.

   _____

5. The biggest pumpkin came from North Cambria Pennsylvania.

   _____

DAILY LANGUAGE PRACTICE

Commas

Name _____

Use a comma between a date and a year. *Sara's birthday is March 4, 2000.* Use a comma between the name of a city and state, as in *Columbus, Ohio.*

Are the commas used correctly? Circle *Yes* or *No.*

1. A giant panda cub named Tai Shan was born July, 9 2005.   Yes   No

2. He was born in Washington, D.C.   Yes   No

3. Another giant panda cub was born August 2, 2005.   Yes   No

4. It was born in, San Diego California.   Yes   No

5. She was named Su Lin on November 10, 2005.   Yes   No

DAILY LANGUAGE PRACTICE

Week Nine Review

Commas

Name _____

Find the mistakes. Write each sentence correctly on the line.

1. George Washington was born on February 22 1732.

_____

2. The White House is in Washington D.C.

_____

3. Mount Rushmore is near Keystone South Dakota.

_____

4. Paul Revere lived in Boston Massachusetts.

_____

5. The American flag was introduced on June 14 1777.

_____

Verb Forms

Name _____

You can add *–ing* to many verbs. The new form describes an action that is happening. If the verb ends in *e*, first drop the *e* and then add *–ing*.

Add *–ing* to each verb. Write the new verb on the line.

1. speak + *–ing*   _____

2. bake + *–ing*   _____

3. fix + *–ing*   _____

4. slide + *–ing*   _____

5. walk + *–ing*   _____

Verb Forms

Name _____

You can add *–ing* to many verbs. The new form describes an action that is happening. If the verb ends in a single vowel and a consonant, double the final consonant when adding *–ing*.

Add *–ing* to each verb to complete the sentence. Write the new verb on the line.

1. The turtles are _____ nests in the sand.
                   (dig)

2. They've laid their eggs, so they are _____ back to sea.
                   (swim)

3. Starlings are _____ their wings overhead.
                   (flap)

4. The sun is _____.
                   (set)

5. Soon the animals will be _____ for the night.
                   (stop)

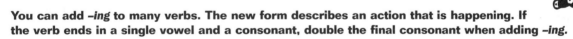

Verb Forms

Week Ten

Name _____

Add *–ed* to many verbs to form the past tense.

Write the past tense of each verb on the line.

1. avoid + *–ed*   _____

2. crash + *–ed*   _____

3. enjoy + *–ed*   _____

4. collect + *–ed*   _____

5. remind + *–ed*   _____

Verb Forms

Week Ten

Name _____

Add *–d* to many verbs that end in *e* to form the past tense.

Write the past tense of each verb on the line.

1. King Tut _____ in Egypt over 3,000 years ago.
         (live)

2. He _____ for 10 years.
         (rule)

3. Tut was about 18 when he _____.
                              (die)

4. Many golden treasures were _____ from his tomb in the 1920s.
                                (remove)

5. These treasures have _____ information about life in ancient Egypt.
                          (provide)

Verb Forms

Name _____

To add *–ed* to a verb that ends in *y*, change the *y* to *i* and add *–ed*. If a verb ends in a single vowel and a consonant, double the final consonant before adding *–ed*.

Add *–ed* to each verb. Write the new verb on the line.

1. supply + *–ed*   _____

2. chop + *–ed*   _____

3. hurry + *–ed*   _____

4. rob + *–ed*   _____

5. bury + *–ed*   _____

Verb Forms

Name _____

Write each sentence correctly on the line.

1. Drew was bullyed by an older student.

   _____

2. The bully teaseed Drew and callled him names.

   _____

3. Sometimes bullying can involve hiting or pushing too.

   _____

4. Drew helpd pass a new law in Maine.

   _____

5. Schools changeed their rules about how they are handleing bullies.

   _____

Contractions

Name _____

Contractions are shortened words that combine two words. *Are* and *not* are combined in the contraction *aren't*. Contractions include apostrophes.

Circle each contraction.

1. A koala doesn't eat just anything.

2. It'll only eat eucalyptus leaves.

3. And that isn't all.

4. It won't eat leaves from some eucalyptus trees.

5. They're very picky eaters!

Contractions

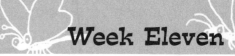

Name _____

Contractions are shortened words that combine two words. *Are* and *not* are combined in the contraction *aren't*. Contractions include apostrophes.

Write the contraction for each pair of words on the lines.

1. does + not _____

2. we + have _____

3. he + is _____

4. was + not _____

5. she + will _____

Contractions

Name _____

Contractions are shortened words that combine two words. *Are* and *not* are combined in the contraction *aren't*. Contractions include apostrophes.

Write the two words that form the contraction on the lines below.

1. didn't   _____ + _____

2. you'll   _____ + _____

3. she's   _____ + _____

4. here's   _____ + _____

5. I'm   _____ + _____

Contractions

Name _____

Contractions are shortened words that combine two words. *Are* and *not* are combined in the contraction *aren't*. Contractions include apostrophes.

Write the contraction for each sentence by combining the words under the line.

1. Coral reefs _____ boring.
                  (are, not)

2. _____ home to many animals.
      (They, are)

3. _____ easy for eels to hide in the reef.
        (It, is)

4. Fish _____ see the eel until too late.
         (do, not)

5. I _____ want to be those fish!
     (would not)

Contractions

Name _____

Contractions are shortened words that combine two words. *Are* and *not* are combined in the contraction *aren't*. Contractions include apostrophes.

Replace the underlined words with a contraction.
Write each sentence correctly on the line.

1. We <u>have not</u> started our project yet.

_____

2. Lynn said <u>she would</u> write the report.

_____

3. <u>I will</u> illustrate it.

_____

4. <u>You have</u> got to present it to the class.

_____

5. Tyler <u>will not</u> be at school that day.

_____

Contractions

Name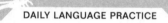

Find the mistakes. Write each sentence correctly on the line.

1. Whats Mount Rushmore?

_____

2. Its a rock that has the faces of four presidents carved in it.

_____

3. The faces on Mount Rushmore had'nt been cleaned in years.

_____

4. Cleaning the faces wasnt an easy job.

_____

5. Now, theyr'e squeaky-clean!

_____

Spelling (Initial and Final Blends)

Name _____

Some words begin or end with consonant blends. Consonant blends are two or more consonants whose sounds blend together. Some blends—like *sc* and *sk*— have the same sound, even though they are spelled differently.

Circle the correct spelling.

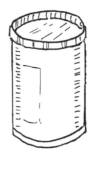

1.   drink   drik

2.   skore   score

3.   skarf   scarf

4.   scared   skeered

5.   blast   balast

© Weekly Reader Corp.

Spelling (Initial and Final Blends)

Name _____

Some words begin or end with consonant blends. Consonant blends are two or more consonants whose sounds blend together. Some blends—like *sc* and *sk*— have the same sound, even though they are spelled differently.

Rearrange the letters to spell a word. Use the clue to help.

1. M S S A H

   _____   *clue:* to crush or break

2. K I T N H

   _____   *clue:* to use your brain

3. B K I N L

   _____   *clue:* to close your eyelid quickly

4. B R M C U E L

   _____   *clue:* to break into small pieces

5. L S A H F

   _____   *clue:* a sudden burst of light

© Weekly Reader Corp.

Spelling (Initial and Final Blends)

3

Name _____

Some words begin or end with consonant blends. Consonant blends are two or more consonants whose sounds blend together. Some blends—like *sc* and *sk*—have the same sound, even though they are spelled differently.

Read each clue. Then circle the correctly spelled answer.

1. Wonderful

   grand   grande

2. Enough to go around

   plenti   plenty

3. To clean well

   skrub   scrub

4. Thin cord

   string   sting

5. Scatter

   sprickle   sprinkle

Spelling (Initial and Final Blends)

4

Name _____

Some words begin or end with consonant blends. Listen carefully for all the sounds in the words.

Circle the correct spelling.

1.   beehind   behind

2.   dream   dreem

3.   gifte   gift

4.   terunk   trunk

5.   young   younk

Spelling (Initial and Final Blends)

Name _____

Some words begin or end with consonant blends. Listen carefully for all the sounds in the words.

Rearrange the letters to spell a word. Use the clue to help.

1. I R G N

   _____   *clue:* jewelry for a finger

2. L N B E G O

   _____   *clue:* to be part of

3. A D N R O G

   _____   *clue:* fire-breathing animal

4. P T U H M

   _____   *clue:* loud noise

5. T P R A N E

   _____   *clue:* mother or father

Spelling (Initial and Final Blends)

Name _____

Find the mistakes. Write the sentences correctly on the lines.

1. The teacher showed the klass how to make skreen prints.

   _____

2. One studnet made a blue printe.

   _____

3. Another used green inke.

   _____

4. One gril decided to painte her picture.

   _____

5. Someone else used a stammp.

   _____

Monthly Review

Name _____

3

A. Find the mistakes. Write each sentence correctly on the line.

1. May 10 1869, was a grande day!

_____

2. At Promontory Utah, the last spike joind two American railroads.

_____

3. Workers began bilding the Central Pacific railroad in California on October 26 1863.

_____

4. About a munth later, the Union Pacific broke ground in Omaha Nebraska.

_____

5. People across America celebrateed the quik new way of travell.

_____

B. Add the ending to the word. Then use the new word in a sentence.

1. hurry + –ing = _____

_____

2. locate + –ed = _____

_____

3. bury + –es = _____

_____

4. library + –es = _____

_____

5. fly + –ing = _____

_____

C. Choose a word from Box A. Combine it with a word from Box B to form a contraction. Write the contractions correctly on the lines. Use each word at least once.

A	B
he	would
should	not
you	will
I	have
they	is

_____

_____

_____

_____

_____

DAILY LANGUAGE PRACTICE

Commas

Name _____

Use commas to separate words in a series. *The sky is clear, bright, and blue.*

Are commas used correctly? Write *Yes* or *No* on the line.

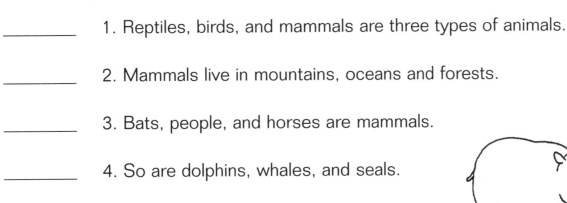

_____ 1. Reptiles, birds, and mammals are three types of animals.

_____ 2. Mammals live in mountains, oceans and forests.

_____ 3. Bats, people, and horses are mammals.

_____ 4. So are dolphins, whales, and seals.

_____ 5. Elephants, hippos and rhinos, are large land mammals.

DAILY LANGUAGE PRACTICE

Commas

Name _____

Use commas to separate words in a series. *The sky is clear, bright, and blue.*

**Each sentence is missing at least one comma.
Write each sentence correctly on the line.**

1. Ben reads about snakes, alligators and crocodiles.

   _____

2. Iris reads about stars planets and moons.

   _____

3. Carlos studies rocks leaves, and insects.

   _____

4. Riley collects shells feathers and seeds.

   _____

5. Ben, Iris Carlos and Riley like science.

   _____

Commas

Name _____

Use commas to separate words in a series. *The sky is clear, bright, and blue.*

Are commas used correctly? Write *Yes* or *No* on the line. Then circle any commas that are in the wrong place. Add commas where they are needed.

_____ 1. California Nevada and Idaho often have wildfires.

_____ 2. Wildfires have also burned Texas, New Mexico, and Arizona.

_____ 3. The fires are started by lightning, the sun, or people.

_____ 4. Dry, grass, leaves and trees catch fire quickly.

_____ 5. Smoke jumpers take tools food and water, with them.

Commas

Name _____

Use commas to separate words in a series. *The sky is clear, bright, and blue.*

**Each sentence is missing at least one comma.
Write each sentence correctly on the line.**

1. Oaks, maples and elms have green leaves in the summer.

_____

2. Their leaves turn yellow red and orange in the fall.

_____

3. The roots trunks, and branches of the trees can live through winter.

_____

4. Spring sunshine warms the air, ground and trees.

_____

5. Leaves use sunlight water and air to make food for the trees.

_____

7

DAILY LANGUAGE PRACTICE

Commas

Name _____

5

Use commas to separate words in a series. *The sky is clear, bright, and blue.*

Does a comma belong in the box? Write *Yes* or *No* on the line.

_____ 1. The canopy, understory ☐ and forest floor are layers of the rain forest.

_____ 2. The forest floor ☐ is home to ants, tapirs, and anteaters.

_____ 3. Snakes, jaguars, and frogs ☐ live in the understory.

_____ 4. You can see sloths ☐ monkeys, and butterflies in the canopy.

_____ 5. Eagles, parrots, and hummingbirds ☐ fly above the rain forest.

DAILY LANGUAGE PRACTICE

Commas

Name _____

Write each sentence correctly on the line.

1. Hurricanes, tornados, and blizzards, are big storms.

_____

2. These storms can bring wind, rain or snow.

_____

3. People need to have food water, and flashlights ready.

_____

4. Sometimes people stay at a school hotel or other safe place.

_____

5. Roads, homes and buildings may need to be fixed.

_____

Subject-Verb Agreement

Name _____

Use a singular verb when the subject is only one. *The bird sings.* Use a plural verb when the subject is more than one. *The birds sing.*

Write the correct word on the line.

1. Male crocodiles _____ loudly to attract females.
   (bellow, bellows)

2. A mother crocodile _____ her nest.
   (guard, guards)

3. The father _____ nearby.
   (stay, stays)

4. Mother crocodiles _____ their young in their mouth.
   (carry, carries)

5. A baby crocodile _____ insects and fish.
   (eat, eats)

© Weekly Reader Corp.

Subject-Verb Agreement

Name _____

Use a singular verb when the subject is only one. *The bird sings.* Use a plural verb when the subject is more than one. *The birds sing.*

Write a word from the box on the line to complete each sentence.

1. Telescopes _____ used to study planets.

2. Do you _____ the planets' names?

3. Mercury _____ closest to the sun.

4. We _____ on Earth.

5. Saturn _____ rings.

know

live

are

has

is

© Weekly Reader Corp.

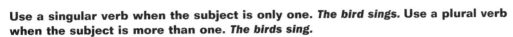

Subject-Verb Agreement

3

Name _____

Use a singular verb when the subject is only one. *The bird sings.* Use a plural verb when the subject is more than one. *The birds sing.*

The subjects and verbs below do not agree.
Write each sentence correctly on the line.

1. Rain fall from clouds.

_____

2. Too much rain cause floods.

_____

3. Lightning storms is dangerous.

_____

4. A blizzard are a big snowstorm.

_____

5. Radar help predict the weather.

_____

Subject-Verb Agreement

4

Name _____

Use a singular verb when the subject is only one. *The bird sings.* Use a plural verb when the subject is more than one. *The birds sing.*

Write the correct word on the line.

1. Chipmunks _____ little striped squirrels.
   (is, are)

2. They _____ on seeds and nuts.
   (nibble, nibbles)

3. A chipmunk _____ a whistling sound.
   (make, makes)

4. It _____ food to eat during the winter.
   (store, stores)

5. Chipmunks _____ burrows in the ground.
   (dig, digs)

Subject-Verb Agreement

Name _____

Use a singular verb when the subject is only one. *The bird sings.* Use a plural verb when the subject is more than one. *The birds sing.*

Write the correct word on the line.

1. The great apes _____ in danger of becoming extinct.
   (is, are)

2. Gorillas, chimpanzees, and orangutans _____ to the great ape family.
   (belong, belongs)

3. Only the orangutan _____ in Asia.
   (live, lives)

4. Africa _____ home to gorillas and chimps.
   (is, are)

5. The apes _____ many threats—most of them from humans.
   (face, faces)

Subject-Verb Agreement

Name _____

Find the mistakes. Write each sentence correctly on the line.

1. The U.S. Treasury make our paper money.

_____

2. A government bank store the bills in a vault where they will be safe.

_____

3. Trained guards delivers the bills to local banks.

_____

4. People spends the money in stores.

_____

5. The government shred the bills when they are worn out.

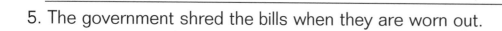

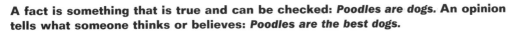

DAILY LANGUAGE PRACTICE

Fact and Opinion

Week Fifteen

Name _____

A fact is something that is true and can be checked: *Poodles are dogs.* An opinion tells what someone thinks or believes: *Poodles are the best dogs.*

Write an F on the line if the sentence is a fact. Write an O on the line if the sentence is an opinion.

_____ 1. Basketball is the most exciting sport.

_____ 2. The National Basketball Association oversees professional basketball.

_____ 3. Thirty teams compete in the NBA.

_____ 4. I think Michael Jordan is the best basketball player ever.

_____ 5. Women play professional basketball too.

© Weekly Reader Corp.

Week Fifteen

DAILY LANGUAGE PRACTICE

Fact and Opinion

Name _____

A fact is something that is true and can be checked: *Poodles are dogs.* An opinion tells what someone thinks or believes: *Poodles are the best dogs.*

Write three facts about your neighborhood.
Write two opinions about your neighborhood.

(Facts)

1. _____

2. _____

3. _____

(Opinions)

1. _____

2. _____

© Weekly Reader Corp.

Fact and Opinion

Name _____

A fact is something that is true and can be checked: *Poodles are dogs.* An opinion tells what someone thinks or believes: *Poodles are the best dogs.*

Write an F on the line if the sentence is a fact. Write an O on the line if the sentence is an opinion.

_____ 1. Life was different long ago.

_____ 2. Children of all ages were in the same classroom.

_____ 3. It was easier to learn back then.

_____ 4. Girls helped with the sewing and cooking.

_____ 5. That was more fun than chores today.

Fact and Opinion

Name _____

A fact is something that is true and can be checked: *Poodles are dogs.* An opinion tells what someone thinks or believes: *Poodles are the best dogs.*

Write an F on the line if the sentence is a fact.
Write an O on the line if the sentence is an opinion.

_____ 1. Mars is the most interesting planet in our solar system.

_____ 2. Mars is called the Red Planet because its soil is a reddish color.

_____ 3. Aliens live on Mars.

_____ 4. It stays very cold on Mars.

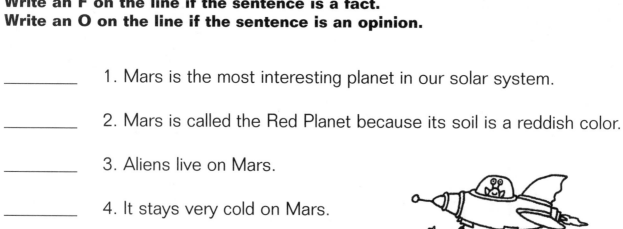

_____ 5. Mars has mountains and valleys.

3

Fact and Opinion

Name _____

A fact is something that is true and can be checked: *Poodles are dogs.* An opinion tells what someone thinks or believes: *Poodles are the best dogs.*

Write an F on the line if the sentence is a fact. Write an O on the line if the sentence is an opinion.

_____ 1. Service dogs help people who have disabilities.

_____ 2. The dogs learn to open and shut doors.

_____ 3. They learn to turn lights on and off.

_____ 4. Service dogs are smarter than other dogs.

_____ 5. They are prettier too.

Fact and Opinion

Name _____

Write an F on the line if the sentence is a fact. Write an O on the line if the sentence is an opinion.

_____ 1. Rosa Parks was a sweet person.

_____ 2. When she refused to give up her seat on the bus, she helped change unfair laws.

_____ 3. Black people didn't ride the buses in Montgomery, Alabama, for more than a year.

_____ 4. Finally, the laws changed to give black people the same rights as white people.

_____ 5. Rosa Parks was the best person to lead the fight for civil rights.

Antonyms

Name _____

Antonyms are words that have opposite meanings.

Are these words antonyms? Write *Yes* or *No* on the line.

_____ 1. sick   well

_____ 2. peace   war

_____ 3. rude   mean

_____ 4. beautiful   fair

_____ 5. clever   foolish

Antonyms

Name _____

Antonyms are words that have opposite meanings.

Write the letter of the word that has an opposite meaning on the line.

_____ 1. easy   a. laugh

_____ 2. empty   b. scared

_____ 3. dull   c. difficult

_____ 4. cry   d. full

_____ 5. brave   e. sharp

5

Week Sixteen

Antonyms

Name _____

Antonyms are words that have opposite meanings.

Write the word from the box with the opposite meaning on the line.

1. enemy   _____

2. bring   _____

3. straight   _____

4. tight   _____

5. deep   _____

crooked
take
shallow
friend
loose

Week Sixteen

Antonyms

Name _____

Antonyms are words that have opposite meanings.

Look at the word in *italics*. Write a word that has an opposite meaning on the line.

1. The homemade cookies were *tasty.*

_____

2. Some rocks have a *smooth* surface.

_____

3. Gymnasts have *strong* muscles.

_____

4. Is the baby *asleep?*

_____

5. You have to *whisper* in the library.

_____

Antonyms

Name _____

Antonyms are words that have opposite meanings.

Find a word that has the opposite meaning as the word in *italics*. Write the antonym on the line.

1. Snow skiing is a _____ weather sport.
   warm

2. Downhill skiing is the _____ ski race.
   slowest

3. Snowboards are _____ than skis.
   narrower

4. The luge is a _____ winter sledding sport.
   safe

5. _____ air helps ski jumpers make longer jumps.
   thick

dangerous
wider
Thin
cold
fastest

© Weekly Reader Corp.

Antonyms

Name _____

Circle the antonyms in each sentence.

1. The gym was noisy when the game started, but it soon grew quiet.

2. If I can't find my notebook, I'll lose the results of my experiment.

3. I wanted to get to class early, but now I'm running late.

4. Do you like to lead or follow when you go hiking?

5. We all looked clumsy next to the graceful dancer.

© Weekly Reader Corp.

Monthly Review

Name _____

A. Find the mistakes. Write each sentence correctly on the line.

1. My favorite subjects is math science and reading.

   _____

2. I is always checking out books from the library.

   _____

3. Last week I picks out books about spiders comets and dinosaurs.

   _____

4. The librarian like to see me reading so many books.

   _____

5. Tomorrow I may surprise her and checks out a mystery!

   _____

B. Find four pairs of antonyms in the puzzle. Look across and down. Write the antonyms on the lines below.

R	E	P	U	Z	W
T	S	E	L	L	O
E	L	O	U	D	R
A	E	B	O	B	S
R	Q	U	I	E	T
L	R	Y	P	S	D
Y	C	L	A	T	E

Antonyms

_____ and _____

_____ and _____

_____ and _____

_____ and _____

C. Write three facts about trees on the lines. Write two opinions about trees.

Fact: _____

Fact: _____

Fact: _____

Opinion: _____

Opinion: _____

Adjectives

Name _____

An adjective is a word that describes a noun or pronoun. *Smart, green, scary,* and *tasty* describe people, places, or things.

Is it an adjective? Write *Yes* or *No* on the line.

_____ 1. flashes

_____ 2. bright

_____ 3. electricity

_____ 4. stormy

_____ 5. crackling

Adjectives

Name _____

An adjective is a word that describes a noun or pronoun. *Smart, green, scary,* and *tasty* describe people, places, or things.

Circle the adjective in each pair.

1. cuddly   hug

2. cuts   sharp

3. jump rope   twirling

4. bouncy   ball

5. funny   laughs

DAILY LANGUAGE PRACTICE

Adjectives

3

Name _____

An adjective is a word that describes a noun or pronoun. *Smart, green, scary,* and *tasty* describe people, places, or things.

Circle the adjective in each sentence.

1. Mexico's Volcano of Fire is an active volcano.

2. It has been shooting hot gas into the sky.

3. Scientists have noticed a pattern in recent activity.

4. They expect an explosive eruption in the next 10 years.

5. Scientists are using special tools to watch the volcano.

DAILY LANGUAGE PRACTICE

Adjectives

4

Name _____

An adjective is a word that describes a noun or pronoun. *Smart, green, scary,* and *tasty* describe people, places, or things.

Write the adjective on the line.

1. That bird has an _____ beak.
   (unusual, odor)

2. What a _____ idea!
   (thought, clever)

3. Lions are _____ animals.
   (territory, wild)

4. The clouds brought _____ weather.
   (rainy, thunder)

5. This is a _____ month.
   (busy, calendar)

Adjectives

Name _____

An adjective is a word that describes a noun or pronoun. *Smart, green, scary,* and *tasty* describe people, places, or things.

Circle the adjectives.

1. Madagascar is a large tropical island near Africa.

2. Many rare animals live in its disappearing forests.

3. Scientists just discovered the tiny, wide-eyed mouse lemur.

4. It has a white stripe on its nose and short, rounded ears.

5. It has orange, maroon, and white fur.

Adjectives

Name _____

Find the adjectives. Write them on the lines.

1. Giant pandas live in the bamboo forests of China.

_____   _____

2. The cool forests are found in high mountains.

_____   _____

3. Thick, woolly fur keeps the pandas warm.

_____   _____

4. Strong teeth and muscles help them crunch tough stalks of bamboo.

_____   _____

5. People love these black and white animals!

_____   _____

1

Week Eighteen

More Verb Forms

Name _____

Some verbs have irregular past tense forms. Some verbs change their vowels in the past tense. The past tense of *sit* is *sat*.

Write the past tense of each verb on the line.

1. sing _____

2. dig _____

3. blow _____

4. draw _____

5. ride _____

Week Eighteen

More Verb Forms

Name _____

Some verbs have irregular past tense forms. Some verbs do not change in the past tense. The past tense of *cut* is *cut*.

Write the correct word on the line.

1. Mom _____ us play with water balloons.
(letted, let)

2. I threw one balloon and _____ the door.
(hit, hitted)

3. It _____ and sprayed water everywhere.
(bursted, burst)

4. I wish I had _____ the door!
(shut, shutted)

5. After that, we _____ playing.
(quitted, quit)

DAILY LANGUAGE PRACTICE

More Verb Forms

3

Name _____

Some verbs have irregular past tense forms. Some past tense verbs end in *–t.*
The past tense of *sleep* is *slept.*

Choose a word from the box. Write the past tense of each verb on the line.

(spent   bent   crept   lost   felt)

1. bend   _____

2. feel   _____

3. spend   _____

4. lose   _____

5. creep   _____

© Weekly Reader Corp.

Week Eighteen

DAILY LANGUAGE PRACTICE

More Verb Forms

4

Name _____

Some verbs have irregular past tense forms. The past tense of *do* is *did.*

Finish each sentence. Write the correct word on the line.

1. Today they break. Yesterday they _____.

2. Today I _____. Yesterday I found.

3. Today you eat. Yesterday you _____.

4. Today we understand. Yesterday we _____.

5. Today I _____. Yesterday I flew.

© Weekly Reader Corp.

More Verb Forms

Name _____

5

Some verbs have irregular past tense forms. Some past tense verbs are shortened. The past tense of *bite* is *bit*.

Find the correct past tense of each verb. Write it on the line.

1. Kelsey _____ the class in stretches.
   (led, leaded)

2. Then Jonathan and Kim _____ teams.
   (choosed, chose)

3. The ball _____ through the air when Tai hit it.
   (shooted, shot)

4. She bumped her nose when she _____ into home base.
   (slid, slided)

5. Her nose _____, but Tai didn't care. She had hit a home run!
   (bleeded, bled)

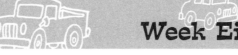

More Verb Forms

Name _____

Find the mistakes. Write each sentence correctly on the line.

1. Martin Luther King Jr. goed to Washington, D.C.

   _____

2. On the steps of the Lincoln Memorial, he maked a speech.

   _____

3. He speaked out for equal rights.

   _____

4. Dr. King sayed that people should be treated fairly.

   _____

5. He teached us that one person can make a difference.

   _____

Possessive Nouns

1

Name _____

A possessive noun uses an apostrophe to show ownership. *The earth's orbit* means the same as *the orbit of Earth.*

Match the phrases with the same meaning. Write the letters on the lines.

_____ 1. the wings of a butterfly   a. a spider's web

_____ 2. the legs of an ant   b. a mosquito's whine

_____ 3. the web of a spider   c. a butterfly's wings

_____ 4. the buzz of a bee   d. an ant's legs

_____ 5. the whine of a mosquito   e. a bee's buzz

Possessive Nouns

2

Name _____

A possessive noun uses an apostrophe to show ownership. *The rose's stem* means the same as *the stem of the rose.*

Each phrase is missing an apostrophe ('). Write the correct phrase on the line.

1. a jellyfishs tentacles

_____

2. a clams shell

_____

3. a sharks fin

_____

4. the divers mask

_____

5. the boats engine

_____

Week Nineteen

Possessive Nouns

Name _____

3

A possessive noun uses an apostrophe to show ownership. *The zoo's animals* were fun to watch. *The zoo's animals* means the same as *animals at the zoo.*

Circle each incorrect possessive noun. Write the word correctly on the line.

1. The childrens trip to the zoo was quite interesting.

   _____

2. They learned that an elephants nose is called a trunk.

   _____

3. A snakes tongue is used to "taste" the air.

   _____

4. The fat stored in a camels hump helps the animal go for a week without water.

   _____

5. An ostrichs kick is so powerful it can kill a lion.

   _____

Week Nineteen

Possessive Nouns

Name _____

4

A possessive noun uses an apostrophe to show ownership. *The family's coats* were ready for winter.

Rewrite each underlined phrase using a possessive noun. Write the new phrase on the line.

1. The <u>leaves of the tree</u> are falling.

   _____

2. The <u>cheeks of the squirrel</u> are full.

   _____

3. The <u>den belonging to the bear</u> is warm.

   _____

4. The <u>cries of the geese</u> fill the air.

   _____

5. <u>Snow of winter</u> covers the ground.

   _____

DAILY LANGUAGE PRACTICE

Possessive Nouns

Name _____

5

A possessive noun uses an apostrophe to show ownership. An apostrophe after a plural noun shows that more than one person or thing owns something. For example: *The men's suits; the ducks' feathers.*

Decide whether the possessive noun is singular or plural. Circle the correct answer.

1. the student's desk   Singular   Plural

2. the children's artwork   Singular   Plural

3. the teachers' workroom   Singular   Plural

4. the book's title   Singular   Plural

5. the classes' program   Singular   Plural

 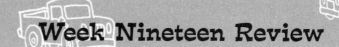

DAILY LANGUAGE PRACTICE

Possessive Nouns

Name _____

Find the mistakes. Write each sentence correctly on the line.

1. The days hike was over, and now it was time to rest.

_____

2. The campers happy shouts echoed across the hillside.

_____

3. The campfires smoke rose through the air.

_____

4. The girls songs welcomed the stars.

_____

5. Soon the nights quiet darkness fell over the camp.

_____

Spelling (Inflected Endings)

Name _____

1

Add –s to form most plural nouns. If a noun ends in *x, th, sh, ch,* or *ss,* add –es to form the plural. *Thumb* becomes *thumbs,* while *dress* becomes *dresses.*

Circle the word that is NOT spelled correctly. Write it correctly on the line.

1. My friendes came over yesterday.

   _____

2. We made valentinees for our class party.

   _____

3. Then we decorated mailboxs.

   _____

4. The biggest one was 15 inchs square!

   _____

5. We had crackeres and fruit for a snack.

   _____

Spelling (Inflected Endings)

Name _____

2

If a noun or verb ends in *y,* change the *y* to *i* before adding –es. *Dry* becomes *dries.*

Add –es to each word. Write the correctly spelled word on the line.

1. fly _____

2. penny _____

3. lady _____

4. party _____

5. daisy _____

Spelling (Inflected Endings)

Name _____

3

To add *–ed* to a word that ends in *e*, simply add *–d*. *Close* becomes *closed*.

Add *–ed* to each word. Then use the correctly spelled word in a sentence.

1. hope _____

   _____

2. smile _____

   _____

3. divide _____

   _____

4. save _____

   _____

5. move _____

   _____

Spelling (Inflected Endings)

Name _____

4

Add *–s* to form most plural nouns. If a noun ends in *x, th, sh, ch,* or *ss,* add *–es* to form the plural. To add *–es* to a word that ends in *e,* simply add *–s.* If a noun or verb ends in *y,* change the *y* to *i* before adding *–es.*

Circle the word that is NOT spelled correctly. Write the word correctly on the line.

1. Our school collected blanketes for the homeless.

   _____

2. We gathered other supplys as well.

   _____

3. One student brought in 50 paires of socks!

   _____

4. Many companys made donations.

   _____

5. Our teachers knew the addresss for the drop-off locations.

   _____

DAILY LANGUAGE PRACTICE

Spelling (Inflected Endings)

5

Name _____

To add *–ing* to a word that ends in silent e, drop the e before adding *–ing*. **Shine** becomes **shining**. If the word ends in y, simply add *–ing*. **Fly** becomes **flying**.

Add *–ing* to each word. Write the correctly spelled word on the line.

1. cry _____

2. shake _____

3. escape _____

4. hurry _____

5. blame _____

DAILY LANGUAGE PRACTICE

Spelling (Inflected Endings)

Name _____

Find the mistakes. Write the sentences correctly on the lines.

1. Sloths live in the junglees of South America.

   _____

2. They are the slowest-moveing mammals in the world.

   _____

3. They spend most of their time hanging upside down from branchs.

   _____

4. Colonys of green algae grow on their fur.

   _____

5. Harpy eagles are natural enemys of the sloth.

Monthly Review

Name _____

5

A. Find the mistakes. Write each sentence correctly on the line.

1. My friends voice is beautiful.

   _____

2. She singed at the schools concert last night.

   _____

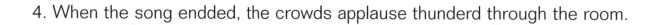

3. The crowd growed quiet, listening.

   _____

4. When the song endded, the crowds applause thunderd through the room.

   _____

5. Sarahs back straightened with pride as she moveed off the stage.

   _____

B. Complete this puzzle. Each answer is an adjective.

Across

2. Smooth

4. _____ as a fox

5. On one's own

8. Nice, easy to be around

9. Without a sound

10. Once upon a time in a
    _____ land...

Down

1. Happening not long ago

3. Opposite of *thin*

6. Liked by everyone

7. Opposite of *messy*

DAILY LANGUAGE PRACTICE

Adverbs

Name _____

An adverb describes a verb, an adjective, or another adverb. An adverb tells
how, when, or where an action took place. *Quickly, now,* and *there* are adverbs.

Is the word in italics an adverb? Write *Yes* or *No* on the line.

_____ 1. The firefighters entered the house *carefully*.

_____ 2. They could see the *angry* red flames through the window.

_____ 3. They didn't want to get trapped *inside*.

_____ 4. They used hoses to *spray* the house with water.

_____ 5. *Finally*, the fire was out.

DAILY LANGUAGE PRACTICE

Adverbs

Name _____

An adverb describes a verb, an adjective, or another adverb. An adverb tells how,
when, or where an action took place. *Quickly, yesterday,* and *outdoors* are adverbs.

Circle the adverb in each pair.

1. gently   gentle

2. often   rock

3. left   correctly

4. them   there

5. bravely   scared

Adverbs

Name _____

An adverb describes a verb, an adjective, or another adverb. An adverb tells how, when, or where an action took place. *Quickly, now,* and *there* are adverbs.

Circle the adverb in each sentence.

1. Amazingly, some people live in space!

2. Two or three astronauts at a time usually live in the International Space Station.

3. Part of their job is to do science experiments and carefully track the results.

4. Sometimes, the astronauts go on space walks.

5. The astronauts have to exercise regularly to keep their muscles strong.

Adverbs

Name _____

An adverb describes a verb, an adjective, or another adverb. You can often form adverbs by adding *–ly* to adjectives.

Add *–ly* to each word in *italics*. Then write it on the line.

1. Mom brought the car _____ to a stop.
   safe

2. The man _____ turned away when we asked him a question.
   rude

3. The friends greeted each other _____.
   warm

4. We _____ thought we would win.
   foolish

5. The stars shone _____ in the night sky.
   bright

Adverbs

Name _____

An adverb describes a verb, an adjective, or another adverb. You can often form adverbs by adding *–ly* to adjectives. If the adjective ends in *y*, change the *y* to *i* before adding *–ly*. For example, *pretty* becomes *prettily*.

Change each adjective to an adverb. Write it on the line. Then write a sentence using the adverb.

1. happy _____

_____

2. busy _____

_____

3. speedy _____

_____

4. hungry _____

_____

5. angry _____

_____

Adverbs

Name _____

Write the adverb in each sentence on the line.

1. Most people were sleeping soundly during the early hours of April 18, 1906.

_____

2. Suddenly, the earth shifted and buildings shook throughout San Francisco.

_____

3. Fires started shortly after the earthquake.

_____

4. For days, the fires burned uncontrollably.

_____

5. Finally, the fires were put out and people started rebuilding the city.

_____

Complete Sentences

Name _____

A complete sentence has a subject and a predicate. The subject names who or what the sentence is about. The predicate tells what the subject is or does.

Decide whether the words in *italics* are the subject or the predicate. Write *S* or *P* on the line.

_____ 1. The planets in our solar system *orbit the sun*.

_____ 2. *Scientists* used to believe that there were nine planets.

_____ 3. Now astronomers *have found what may be a tenth planet*.

_____ 4. They *named it Sedna*.

_____ 5. *Sedna* is about the size of Pluto.

Complete Sentences

Name _____

A complete sentence has a subject and a predicate. The subject names who or what the sentence is about. The predicate tells what the subject is or does.

Circle the subject. Underline the predicate.

1. Danny Way leaped over the Great Wall of China on a skateboard.

2. He used a ramp that he brought from California.

3. Danny was going nearly 50 miles (80 km) per hour over the wall.

4. Parts of the Great Wall are more than 2,000 years old.

5. The wall is about 4,000 miles (6,436 km) long.

DAILY LANGUAGE PRACTICE

Complete Sentences

3

Name _____

A complete sentence has a subject and a predicate. A sentence fragment is missing a subject, a verb, or both.

Is the sentence complete? Write *Yes* or *No* on the line.

_____ 1. Brave visitors to the Grand Canyon.

_____ 2. Plans are being made to build a glass walkway.

_____ 3. The walkway will stick out 70 feet (21 m) from the edge of the canyon.

_____ 4. Visitors can look down at the Colorado River 4,000 feet (1,220 m) below.

_____ 5. Carved by the Colorado River over millions of years.

DAILY LANGUAGE PRACTICE

Complete Sentences

4

Name _____

A complete sentence has a subject and a predicate. A sentence fragment is missing a subject, a verb, or both.

Use each sentence fragment to write a complete sentence. Many answers are possible.

1. The bright-eyed squirrels.

_____

2. Enjoying the warm sunshine.

_____

3. The scent of the pine trees.

_____

4. When the jays started chattering.

_____

5. Rustled the leaves.

_____

Complete Sentences

5

Name _____

A complete sentence has a subject and a verb. A sentence fragment is missing a subject, a verb, or both. Sometimes you can combine two fragments to create a complete sentence.

Combine these sentence fragments. Write complete sentences on the line.

1. On August 29, Hurricane Katrina. Hit the Gulf Coast.

   _____

2. The fierce storm. Destroyed buildings, homes, and trees.

   _____

3. After Katrina passed. Most of New Orleans, Louisiana, was flooded.

   _____

4. Cleanup after Katrina. Is expected to take months or even years.

   _____

5. People across America. Have reached out to people hurt by Katrina.

   _____

Complete Sentences

Name _____

Write each sentence correctly on the line.

1. With a wave of his wand. Harry Potter has put kids under his spell.

   _____

2. Millions of kids. Lined up to buy the sixth book in the series.

   _____

3. Kids today are going wild. For books about magical worlds.

   _____

4. Many of the books. Are being turned into movies.

   _____

5. Do you think? That the books are casting a spell on people?

   _____

Pronouns

Name _____

A pronoun is a word that replaces a noun. Use a subject pronoun to replace a noun that is the subject of a sentence.

Write the subject pronoun on the line.

1. _____ are going camping.
   (Us, We)

2. _____ is bringing the tent.
   (He, Him)

3. _____ are packing the food.
   (They, Them)

4. _____ have the flashlights.
   (Me, I)

5. _____ will tell stories when it gets dark.
   (She, Her)

Pronouns

Name _____

A pronoun is a word that replaces a noun. Use a subject pronoun to replace a noun that is the subject of a sentence.

| We | She | He |
| They | It | |

Choose a pronoun from the box to replace the underlined words in each sentence. Write the correct pronoun on the line.

1. <u>Dr. Charles R. Drew</u> discovered a way to store blood until it was needed.

   _____

2. <u>Marian Anderson</u> entertained millions with her beautiful voice.

   _____

3. <u>Jesse Owens and Arthur Ashe</u> made sports headlines in track and tennis.

   _____

4. <u>You and I</u> have learned a lot. _____

5. <u>African American history</u> is interesting. _____

Pronouns

Name _____

A pronoun is a word that replaces a noun. When using the pronoun *I* in a sentence, always name yourself last. *Mom and I went to the movies.*

Write each sentence correctly on the line.

1. Me and Kate planted seeds in the garden.

_____

2. Tim and me watered the seeds.

_____

3. I and Kate pulled the weeds.

_____

4. Me and Tim dug up the carrots.

_____

5. Kate, Tim, and me washed and ate the carrots.

_____

© Weekly Reader Corp.

Pronouns

Name _____

A pronoun is a word that replaces a noun. Use an object pronoun to replace a noun in the predicate.

Choose a pronoun from the box to replace the underlined words in each sentence. Write the correct pronoun on the line. (You may use a pronoun more than once.)

| him |
| her |
| it |
| us |
| them |

1. Don't be late for <u>your appointment</u>. _____

2. You need to let <u>Dr. Ann Cho</u> check your teeth. _____

3. Tell <u>your mom and me</u> when you are ready to go. _____

4. We will take <u>your brother</u> too. _____

5. You need to have <u>your teeth</u> checked twice a year. _____

© Weekly Reader Corp.

Week Twenty-Three

Pronouns

Name _____

A pronoun is a word that replaces a noun. Use an object pronoun to replace a noun that is a direct object.

Write the correct word on the line.

1. Did your teacher tell _____ about Lewis and Clark?
   (you, your)

2. They explored the West. They traveled through much of _____ on rivers.
   (it, its)

3. Lewis took his dog with _____ on the trip.
   (him, he)

4. An Indian woman named Sacagawea went with _____ .
   (they, them)

5. People also called _____ Bird Woman.
   (she, her)

Week Twenty-Three Review

Pronouns

Name _____

Write each sentence correctly on the line.

1. Me and my friends have some tiny silkworm eggs.

   _____

2. It is hard to see they.

   _____

3. Them hatched into little caterpillars.

   _____

4. Us fed the caterpillars mulberry leaves.

   _____

5. Then we watched one as its made a cocoon.

   _____

Comparatives and Superlatives

Name _____

Some adjectives are used to compare. Add *–er* to an adjective if you are comparing two things. For example: The pine tree is *taller* than I am.

Choose the correct word. Write it on the line.

1. Polar bears live in _____ places.
   (colder, cold)

2. They are _____ than other bears.
   (larger, large)

3. Male polar bears are _____ than females.
   (heavier, heavy)

4. Their _____ fur keeps them warm.
   (thick, thicker)

5. In the spring, the bears sleep _____ during the day than at night.
   (longer, long)

Comparatives and Superlatives

Name _____

Some adjectives are used to compare. Use the *–est* suffix if you are comparing more than two things. For example: That is the *tallest* tree.

Choose the correct word. Write it on the line.

1. The _____ (tall, tallest) dinosaur ever found was the Sauroposeidon.

2. The Diplodocus had the _____ (long, longest) tail.

3. The _____ (larger, largest) Tyrannosaurus rex skeleton ever found was discovered in South Dakota.

4. Stegosaurus was large, but it had the _____ (small, smallest) brain of all.

5. The Dromiceiomimus, a bird-like dinosaur, could probably run the _____ (faster, fastest).

Comparatives and Superlatives

3

Name _____

Some adjectives are used to compare. Although some end in –er or –est, others do not. Use *better*, *more*, and *less* to compare two things. Use *best*, *most*, and *least* to compare more than two things.

Choose the correct word. Write it on the line.

1. Kim has _____ marbles than Lei.
   (more, most)

2. Scott's paper airplane flew _____ than Steve's.
   (gooder, better)

3. We got _____ rain today than yesterday.
   (less, least)

4. That was the _____ fish I've ever tasted!
   (goodest, best)

5. Brussels sprouts are my _____ favorite vegetable.
   (less, least)

Comparatives and Superlatives

4

Name _____

Add –r or –st to adjectives that end in –e to form new adjectives. For example, *nice* becomes *nicer* or *nicest*.

Write the new adjectives on the lines.

	(+ –r)	(+ –st)
1. safe	_____	_____
2. late	_____	_____
3. nice	_____	_____
4. gentle	_____	_____
5. simple	_____	_____

Comparatives and Superlatives

Name _____

If an adjective has two syllables and ends in *y*, change the *y* to *i*. Then add –*er* or –*est* to form a new adjective. For example, *happy* becomes *happier* or *happiest*.

Circle the adjective that is spelled correctly.

1.   itchyer   itchier

2.   craziest   crazyest

3.   rainyer   rainier

4.   trickyest   trickiest

5.   laziest   lazyest

Comparatives and Superlatives

Name _____

Find the mistakes. Write the sentence correctly on the line.

1. Taiwan is an island near China. It is smallest than Japan.

_____

2. The island is about 90 miles (145 km) at its wideest point.

_____

3. The mountains are the rainyest part of the island.

_____

4. The world's taller building is in Taiwan.

_____

5. Some people think that Taiwanese opera is gooder than the movies.

_____

Monthly Review

Name _____

A. Find the mistakes. Write each sentence correctly on the line.

1. Much of the continent of Africa. Is a grassland.

_____

2. Mr. Richards say it is home to many different animals.

_____

3. Him told us that giraffes are the taller animal in the world.

_____

4. Once, Mr. Richards. Saw they running across the plains.

_____

5. Lions live in a pride. Live in Africa too.

_____

B. Fill in adverbs to complete the sentences. Many answers are possible.

Kay and Tim _____ begged their parents to take them to the

circus. _____, it was the last day. _____,

Mom and Dad agreed. The family piled _____ in the car. Mom

_____ parked the car. Dad stood in line _____.

With tickets in hand, the four _____ walked into the big top.

C. Find five comparative or superlative adjectives in this puzzle. Look across and down. Then use each one in a sentence on the lines below.

P	Y	M	K	O	B	H	L
B	O	U	N	C	I	E	R
E	W	D	V	A	G	M	I
O	L	D	E	R	G	D	A
T	T	I	N	I	E	S	T
L	F	E	O	S	R	K	D
A	P	S	B	C	S	A	Z
R	E	T	W	O	R	C	A

_____

_____

_____

_____

Prefixes

Name _____

A prefix is a part of a word. It is added to the beginning of a base word. A prefix changes the meaning of the base word. The prefix *un–* means "not" or "the opposite of." *Un– + real = unreal* ("not real").

Add the prefix *un–* to each word. Write the meaning of the new word on the line.

1. *un–* + lock = _____

   meaning: _____

2. *un–* + cover = _____

   meaning: _____

3. *un–* + healthy = _____

   meaning: _____

4. *un–* + comfortable = _____

   meaning: _____

5. *un–* + known = _____

   meaning: _____

© Weekly Reader Corp.

Prefixes

Name _____

A prefix is a part of a word. It is added to the beginning of a base word. A prefix changes the meaning of a base word. The prefix *re–* means "do again." *Re– + read = reread* ("to read again").

Add the prefix *re–* to each word. Use the new word in a sentence. Write the sentence on the line.

1. *re–* + do = _____

   _____

2. *re–* + fill = _____

   _____

3. *re–* + take = _____

   _____

4. *re–* + glue = _____

   _____

5. *re–* + trace = _____

© Weekly Reader Corp.

5

Prefixes

Name _____

A prefix is a part of a word. It is added to the beginning of a base word. A prefix changes the meaning of a base word. The prefixes *im–* and *in–* mean "not." *Im–* + *possible* = *impossible* ("not possible").

Add the prefix *im–* or *in–* to each word.
Write the meaning of the new word on the line.

1. *im–* + polite = _____
   meaning: _____

2. *im–* + proper = _____
   meaning: _____

3. *in–* + active = _____
   meaning: _____

4. *in–* + complete = _____
   meaning: _____

5. *im–* + patient = _____
   meaning: _____

Prefixes

Name _____

A prefix is a part of a word. It is added to the beginning of a base word. A prefix changes the meaning of a base word. The prefix *dis–* means "not" or "the opposite of." *Dis–* + *loyal* = *disloyal* ("not loyal").

Add the prefix *dis–* to each word. Use the new word in a sentence.
Write the sentence on the line.

1. *dis–* + agree = _____
   _____

2. *dis–* + appear = _____
   _____

3. *dis–* + approve = _____
   _____

4. *dis–* + honest = _____
   _____

5. *dis–* + comfort = _____
   _____

Prefixes

Name _____

Prefixes can tell how many. For instance, the prefixes *uni–* and *mono–* mean "one." *Mono– + rail = monorail* ("one rail or track").

Decide what each prefix means.
Write the number in the blank.

1. bicycle _____ wheels   *bi–* means _____

2. century _____ years   *cent–* means _____

3. triangle _____ angles   *tri–* means _____

4. octopus _____ tentacles   *oct–* means _____

5. pentagon _____ sides   *penta–* means _____

Prefixes

Name _____

Replace the underlined words with a word that has a prefix.
Write each sentence correctly on the line.

1. The report was full of facts that were <u>not important</u>.

_____

2. The students had to <u>write</u> the report <u>again</u>.

_____

3. They were <u>not pleased</u>.

_____

4. They thought the task was <u>not possible</u>.

_____

5. They finally <u>started again</u>.

DAILY LANGUAGE PRACTICE

Quotation Marks

1

Name _____

Use quotation marks around someone's exact words. *"Welcome to school," said the principal.* Remember that punctuation marks go inside the quotation marks.

Is each sentence punctuated correctly? Write *Yes* or *No* on the line.

_____ 1. "First, dig a hole for your seed," said the teacher.

_____ 2. "Is everyone ready? she asked."

_____ 3. "Can we cover the seed with dirt now?" asked Kylie.

_____ 4. "Yes," and water it lightly, answered the teacher.

_____ 5. "Then we sit back and watch them grow!" exclaimed Tom.

DAILY LANGUAGE PRACTICE

Quotation Marks

2

Name _____

Use quotation marks around someone's exact words. *"Welcome to school," said the principal.* Remember that punctuation marks go inside the quotation marks.

These sentences are missing quotation marks. Rewrite each sentence correctly on the line.

1. Let's help with the coastal cleanup this year, suggested Maddie.

_____

2. That's a great idea! Dad replied.

_____

3. Last year volunteers picked up lots of trash, Matt added.

_____

4. That trash can kill birds and other animals, Mom said.

_____

5. I'll get our gloves and trash bags! Maddie exclaimed.

Quotation Marks

Name _____

3

Use quotation marks around someone's exact words. *"Welcome to school!" said the principal. "Thank you," replied the student.* Remember that punctuation marks go inside the quotation marks.

Is each sentence punctuated correctly? Write *Yes* or *No* on the line.

_____ 1. "This is my report about Chinese New Year, Alex announced."

_____ 2. Did you know that Chinese New Year lasts 15 days? "she asked."

_____ 3. "People visit family and friends," Alex explained.

_____ 4. "The house is decorated with pretty flowers and oranges", she said.

_____ 5. "The last day of the new year is the Lantern Festival!" Alex ended.

Quotation Marks

Name _____

4

Use quotation marks around someone's exact words. *"Welcome to school!" said the principal. "Thank you," replied the student.* Remember that punctuation marks go inside the quotation marks.

These sentences are not punctuated correctly. Rewrite each sentence on the line using correct punctuation.

1. Did you know that we are "studying penguins," Cooper asked his father?

_____

2. "What have you learned? Dad replied."

_____

3. "Four types of penguins live in Antarctica", Cooper said.

_____

4. Early explorers thought they were fish! "he laughed."

_____

5. "They are good swimmers, his father agreed.

_____

Quotation Marks

Name _____

Use quotation marks around someone's exact words. *"Welcome to school!" said the principal. "Thank you,"* replied the student. Remember that punctuation marks go inside the quotation marks.

Is each sentence punctuated correctly? Write *Yes* or *No* on the line.

_____ 1. "Some rocks are rare and very valuable," said the museum guide.

_____ 2. They are called gems," he explained.

_____ 3. "Some common gemstones are diamonds, emeralds, and rubies," he said.

_____ 4. "Did you know that this is the largest diamond in the world" he asked?

_____ 5. "It is called the Star of Africa, he continued."

Quotation Marks

Name _____

Write each sentence correctly on the line.

1. We went to Mesa Verde on vacation this summer," Lynn said.

_____

2. "What's that"? I asked.

_____

3. "It is the home of the Anasazi Indians, she replied.

_____

4. They lived thousands of years ago in cliff dwellings, "continued Lynn."

_____

5. "You can still see their houses today! she exclaimed."

_____

Homophones

Name _____

1

Homophones are words that sound the same, but have different meanings. *Here* and *hear* are homophones.

Write a homophone for each word on the line.

1. aunt _____

2. two _____

3. hour _____

4. meat _____

5. eight _____

Homophones

Name _____

2

Homophones are words that sound the same, but have different meanings. *Here* and *hear* are homophones.

Write the correct word on the line.

1. I _____ how to cook.
      (know, no)

2. She _____ the book.
      (red, read)

3. The _____ was in the woods.
      (deer, dear)

4. There was _____ on the grass.
      (dew, do)

5. Did you _____ the quilt?
      (so, sew)

DAILY LANGUAGE PRACTICE

Homophones

Name _____

Homophones are words that sound the same, but have different meanings. *Here* and *hear* are homophones.

Choose the word that is spelled incorrectly.
Write the correct homophone on the line.

1. The horn blue at the end of the game.

   _____

2. We looked at the score on the bored.

   _____

3. Our team was ahead by ate points.

   _____

4. We had one the game!

   _____

5. We were horse from so much cheering.

   _____

DAILY LANGUAGE PRACTICE

Homophones

Name _____

Homophones are words that sound the same, but have different meanings. *Here* and *hear* are homophones.

Write a homophone for each word on the line.

1. knight _____

2. nose _____

3. week _____

4. pear _____

5. tied _____

DAILY LANGUAGE PRACTICE

Homophones

Name _____

Homophones are words that sound the same, but have different meanings. *Here* and *hear* are homophones.

Write the correct word on the line.

1. I enjoyed our hike _____ the woods.
   (threw, through)

2. We saw several _____.
   (deer, dear)

3. We heard the _____ of tiny birds.
   (cheep, cheap)

4. One _____ past us.
   (flu, flew)

5. We even saw a _____ track near the stream.
   (bear, bare)

Week Twenty-Seven Review

DAILY LANGUAGE PRACTICE

Homophones

Name _____

Find the mistakes. Write each sentence correctly on the line.

1. How wood you rather travel?

   _____

2. Sum people like to drive cars.

   _____

3. Others like to sale their boats.

   _____

4. Riding in a train gives you time to reed a book.

   _____

5. I prefer to fly in a plain.

   _____

Graphic Sources of Information

Name _____

Graphs make it easy to compare information. A picture graph is one kind of graph.

Read the graph to learn the type of leaves collected by the students. Then write your answers on the lines.

Leaves Collected	= 1 leaf
Maple	🍃 🍃 🍃 🍃 🍃 🍃 🍃 🍃
Oak	🍃 🍃 🍃
Birch	🍃 🍃 🍃 🍃 🍃

1. From which tree did the students find the most leaves? _____

2. How many birch and oak leaves were found in all? _____

3. How many more maple leaves than birch leaves were found? _____

4. How many leaves did the students find in all? _____

Graphic Sources of Information

Name _____

Charts provide information in a table form. The headings help you find information quickly.

Read the chart to learn more about elephants. Then write your answers to the questions on the lines.

	African Elephant	Asian Elephant
Average Height	Male: 11 feet Female: 9 feet	Male: 10 feet Female: 8 feet
Weight	Male: Up to 6 tons Female: Up to 4 tons	Male: Up to 4 tons Female: Up to 3 tons
Tusks	Both males and females have tusks	Only males have tusks

1. How tall is the average male Asian elephant? _____

2. Which kind of elephant does not have tusks? _____

3. How much more does a male African elephant weigh than a female? _____

4. Which is the largest elephant? _____

Graphic Sources of Information

Name _____

3

Charts provide information in a table form. The headings help you find information quickly.

Read the chart to learn more about the deepest spots in the oceans. Then write your answers to the questions on the lines.

Location	Ocean	Depth
Mariana Trench	Pacific Ocean	35,827 feet
Puerto Rico Trench	Atlantic Ocean	30,246 feet
Java Trench	Indian Ocean	24,460 feet
Arctic Basin	Arctic Ocean	18,456 feet

1. Which ocean holds the deepest spot? _____

2. Where is the Java Trench found? _____

3. Which trenches are deeper than 30,000 feet? _____

4. Which spot is the least deep? _____

Graphic Sources of Information

Name _____

4

Graphs make it easy to compare information. A bar graph is one kind of graph.

Read the graph to learn more about rivers. Then write your answers to the questions on the lines.

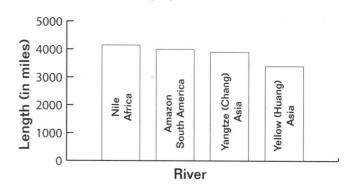

1. Which is the longest river in the world? _____

2. About how long is the Amazon River? _____

3. On which continent is the Nile River located? _____

4. Which river is Asia's longest river? _____

Graphic Sources of Information

Name _____

Charts provide information in a table form. The headings help you find information quickly.

**Read the chart to learn more about insects and spiders.
Then write your answers to the questions on the lines.**

Animal	Number of Legs	Number of Body Parts	Wings?	Antennae?
Insects	6	3	Sometimes	Yes
Spiders	8	2	No	No

1. How many legs does a spider have? _____

2. Which has antennae: spiders or insects? _____

3. Do all insects have wings? _____

4. Which has fewer body parts: spiders or insects? _____

Graphic Sources of Information

Name _____

Charts provide information in a table form. Use the headings to find information quickly.

**Read the chart to learn more about these planets.
Then write your answers to the questions on the lines.**

Planet	Average Distance from the Sun	Length of Day	Length of Year
Earth	93 million miles	24 hours	365 days
Mars	142 million miles	24 hours, 37 minutes (Earth time)	687 Earth days

1. How much longer is a day on Mars than on Earth? _____

2. Which of these planets has the longest year? _____

3. Which of these planets is closest to the sun? _____

4. How much shorter is Earth's year than Mars's year? _____

Monthly Review

Name _____

A. Find the mistakes. Write each sentence correctly on the line.

1. "Please reed your story allowed, said Mr. Kent.

   _____

2. I started to grown, but then eye got to my feat.

   _____

3. The Boy Who Eight Ate Beats, "I began."

   _____

4. I herd laughter brake out around the room.

   _____

5. I grinned, "then I red the rest of the story."

   _____

B. Use the chart to answer the questions.

Costliest Hurricanes (Through 2004)		
Hurricane	Year	Damage
Andrew	1992	$26.5 billion
Charley	2004	$15 billion
Ivan	2004	$14 billion
Frances	2004	$9 billion

1. Which hurricanes caused more than $10 billion in damage?

   _____

2. How many of the four costliest hurricanes occurred in 2004?

   _____

3. How many years after Hurricane Andrew hit did Hurricane Charley hit?

   _____

Commas

Name _____

Use a comma to separate a quotation and the words that tell who said them.
Place the comma inside the quotation marks. *"This is my dad," said Riley.*

The sentences are missing commas. Write the sentences correctly on the lines.

1. "I have swim practice after school" said Samantha.

   _____

2. "My first swim meet is this weekend" she continued.

   _____

3. "I like to swim too" said Kelsey.

   _____

4. "It's my favorite part of the summer" she said.

   _____

5. "Come swim with me" invited Samantha.

   _____

Commas

Name _____

In dialogue, the tag tells who is talking. *Joan said* is the tag in *Joan said, "It's nice to meet you."* When a sentence begins with a tag, use a comma to separate it from the quotation.

The sentences are missing commas. Write the sentences correctly on the lines.

1. Ben yelled "Come look at this gila monster!"

   _____

2. Carmen said "I can't believe that it can eat a bird."

   _____

3. Ben said "Look. It says they're poisonous."

   _____

4. Carmen said "I'm glad they're behind the glass."

   _____

5. Ben said "Me, too!"

   _____

Commas

Name _____

Use a comma to separate a quotation and the words that tell who said it. *"This is my dad," said Riley. Riley said, "This is my dad."*

The sentences are missing commas. Write the sentences correctly on the lines.

1. "Remember that your reports are due tomorrow" said the teacher.

_____

2. Mike said "I'm almost finished."

_____

3. "I have my notes and outline" he said.

_____

4. "I've written my first draft" he went on.

_____

5. Mike declared "All I have to do is check it carefully tonight."

_____

Commas

Name _____

Use commas before and after the names of people who are being spoken to. *Steve, are you done with your homework? Yes, Mom.*

Underline the name of the person being spoken to. Add a comma where it is needed.

1. Julia where is your backpack?

2. Do you have your homework done Kim?

3. Nico this is a well-written story!

4. Katherine let's ride bikes.

5. I'd rather go to the park Lauren.

Commas

Name _____

Use commas before and after the names of people who are being spoken to, even in a quotation. *"Steve, are you done with your homework?" asked Mom.*

These sentences are missing commas. Write each sentence correctly on the line.

1. "Are you going to play soccer this spring Todd?" asked Dan.

   _____

2. Todd replied, "I sure am Dan!"

   _____

3. "How about you Brian?" Todd asked.

   _____

4. "Sure! Let's keep the team together Todd," answered Brian.

   _____

5. Todd asked, "Do you have time for a game now Dan?"

   _____

Commas

Name _____

Find the mistakes. Write the sentences correctly on the lines.

1. "It snowed last night" Miguel said.

   _____

2. "Rosa wake up!" he shouted.

   _____

3. Rosa asked "What's all the shouting about?"

   _____

4. Miguel answered "Look out the window at the snow!"

   _____

5. "Let's build a snowman Miguel" suggested Rosa.

   _____

Titles

Name _____

Capitalize important words in titles. Always capitalize the first and last word. Do not capitalize articles (*a, an, the*), conjunctions (*and, but, or*), or prepositions shorter than five letters (*in, for, near*).

Is each book title capitalized correctly? Write *Yes* or *No* on the line.

_____ 1. *My teacher is an Alien*

_____ 2. *The Best Book Of Sharks*

_____ 3. *Encyclopedia Brown and the Case of the Jumping Frogs*

_____ 4. *The Phantom Tollbooth*

_____ 5. *in the Year of the Boar and Jackie Robinson*

Titles

Name _____

Capitalize important words in titles. Always capitalize the first and last word. Do not capitalize articles (*a, an, the*), conjunctions (*and, but, or*), or prepositions shorter than five letters (*in, for, near*).

Write each movie title correctly on the line.

1. *monsters, inc.*

_____

2. *beauty and the beast*

_____

3. *remember the titans*

_____

4. *back to the future*

_____

5. *lady and the tramp*

_____

Titles

Name _____

Capitalize important words in titles. Always capitalize the first and last word. Do not capitalize articles (*a, an, the*), conjunctions (*and, but, or*), or prepositions shorter than five letters (*in, for, near*).

Is each song title capitalized correctly? Write *Yes* or *No* on the line.

_____ 1. "Puff the Magic Dragon"

_____ 2. "This land is Your land"

_____ 3. "Take Me Out to the Ball Game"

_____ 4. "Home On The Range"

_____ 5. "She'll be Coming Round the Mountain"

Titles

Name _____

Capitalize important words in titles. Underline the titles of books, movies, and plays. For example: We read <u>The Very Hungry Caterpillar.</u>

Write each sentence correctly on the line.

1. Mr. Popper's Penguins made me laugh when I read it.

   _____

2. Sue liked the movie James and the Giant Peach.

   _____

3. We read The Sign of the Beaver in class.

   _____

4. Have you seen Jason and the Argonauts?

   _____

5. My family went to see The King and I.

   _____

Titles

Name _____

Capitalize important words in titles. Use quotation marks around the titles of songs and poems. For example: We sang "Twinkle, Twinkle Little Star."

Write each sentence correctly on the line.

1. My little sister sings I'm a Little Teapot.

_____

2. Over in the Meadow is a counting poem.

_____

3. Home on the Range is an old cowboy song.

_____

4. We memorized Langston Hughes' poem April rain Song.

_____

5. Down by the Bay is one of the silliest songs I know.

_____

Titles

Name _____

Find the mistakes. Write each sentence correctly on the line.

1. One of my favorite books is mrs. Frisby and the rats of NIMH.

_____

2. Eletelephony is a funny poem!

_____

3. We sang You are my sunshine in our program.

_____

4. Have you read my life in dog years by Gary Paulsen?

_____

5. Swiss family robinson was a great movie.

_____

DAILY LANGUAGE PRACTICE

Parts of a Book

1

Name _____

You can find the title, author, and illustrator of a book on the title page.

Use the title pages to answer the questions. Write your answers on the lines.

Charlotte's Web
by E. B. White
Illustrated by
Garth Williams

The Indian in the Cupboard
by Lynne Reid Banks
Illustrated by
Brock Cole

1. Who wrote *The Indian in the Cupboard?* _____

2. What book did Garth Williams illustrate? _____

3. Is Brock Cole an author? _____

4. What book did E. B. White write? _____

5. Who is the illustrator of *The Indian in the Cupboard?* _____

© Weekly Reader Corp.

DAILY LANGUAGE PRACTICE

Parts of a Book

2

Name _____

The table of contents is at the front of the book. The chapter titles tell you what is in a book. They help you decide what pages to read to answer general questions.

Use the table of contents to answer the questions.
Write your answers on the lines.

Table of Contents

1. What is this book about? _____

2. What chapter might tell about spiders in the desert? _____

3. What is Chapter 3 about? _____

4. On what pages can you find the glossary? _____

5. What chapter might tell about funnel webs? _____

© Weekly Reader Corp.

Parts of a Book

Name _____

The glossary is at the back of a book. It provides definitions in alphabetical order for important words.

Use the glossary to answer the questions. Write your answers on the lines.

Glossary	
abdomen	the rear part of the spider's body
egg sac	the pouch of silk that holds a spider's eggs
predator	an animal that hunts or eats another
prey	an animal that is hunted or eaten by another
spiderling	a baby spider
spinneret	the body part that produces silk

1. What is a spiderling? _____

2. What holds a spider's eggs? _____

3. What is a predator? _____

4. What does a spider use to spin its web? _____

5. What is an abdomen? _____

Parts of a Book

Name _____

Use the index to find the pages that answer specific questions. Commas tell you to look on separate pages: *webs, 4, 8* tells you to look on page 4 and page 8 to find information about webs. Dashes tell you to read all the pages: *webs, 4–8* tells you to read pages 4 through 8 to find information about webs.

Index	
black widow, 4	silk, 7, 10
cobweb, 8	spiderling, 12–14
egg sac, 10	spinneret, 7–8, 10
funnel web, 9	tarantula, 6

Use the index to answer the questions. Write your answers on the lines.

1. Which page tells about funnel webs? _____

2. How many pages tell about spiderlings? _____

3. Which page tells about cobwebs? _____

4. On which pages would you find information about silk? _____

5. What topics are found on page 7? _____

Parts of a Book

Name _____

Guide words are used on pages that are arranged in alphabetical order. The word on the left is the first entry on the page. The word on the right is the last entry on the page. Guide words help you find a word quickly.

The guide words on an index page are *egg sac* and *spiderling*. Circle the words that are found on this index page.

1.   spider   spinneret

2.   ballooning   recluse spiders

3.   predator   tarantula

4.   fishing spiders   webs

5.   abdomen   eyes

Parts of a Book

Name _____

Decide which part of the book can be used to answer each question. Write the letter of your answer on the line. (You may use a letter more than once.)

_____   1. Who wrote the book?   a. glossary

_____   2. What is the definition of orbit?   b. index

_____   3. What page does Chapter 4 start on?   c. title page

_____   4. What page tells how a comet's tail forms?   d. table of contents

_____   5. How many chapters are in the book?

Spelling (Commonly Misspelled Words)

Name _____

1

Some words have tricky spelling patterns. Here are some words that students often misspell.

Arrange the letters to spell a word. Use the clue to help.

1. C E P I S L A   *clue:* better than most

_____

2. S R U G A   *clue:* sweet stuff

_____

3. G A A N I   *clue:* once more

_____

4. M N A I L A   *clue:* a pet, for instance

_____

5. H H T I G E   *clue:* the distance from top to bottom

_____

© Weekly Reader Corp.

Spelling (Commonly Misspelled Words)

Name _____

2

Some words have tricky spelling patterns. Here are some words that students often misspell.

Circle the correct spelling.

1.   choclate   chocolate

2.   could   coud

3.   freind   friend

4.   rinkel   wrinkle

5.   always   allways

© Weekly Reader Corp.

Spelling (Commonly Misspelled Words)

Name _____

Some words have tricky spelling patterns. Here are some words that students often misspell.

Circle the word that is NOT spelled correctly. Write the correct spelling on the line.

1. Several casles still stand in Europe.

   _____

2. Seeing them makes you think of nights in armor.

   _____

3. Once, we walked thru one.

   _____

4. A huge pikcher hung on the wall.

   _____

5. The most intresting thing was the bathroom!

   _____

Spelling (Commonly Misspelled Words)

Name _____

Some words have tricky spelling patterns. Here are some words that students often misspell.

Circle the word that is NOT spelled correctly. Write the correct spelling on the line.

1.	calf	folk	brekfast
2.	untill	almost	guess
3.	wrong	wrapp	wrote
4.	lissen	knee	real
5.	believe	whistle	laff

Week Thirty-Two

Spelling (Commonly Misspelled Words)

Name _____

5

Some words have tricky spelling patterns. Here are some words that students often misspell.

Circle the word that is NOT spelled correctly. Write the correct spelling on the line.

1. Daylite was fading fast.

_____

2. I was getting frightned.

_____

3. I wasn't shur where I was.

_____

4. I heard a nock on the door.

_____

5. I allmost jumped out of my skin.

_____

© Weekly Reader Corp.

Week Thirty-Two Review

Spelling (Commonly Misspelled Words)

Name _____

Find the mistakes. Write each sentence correctly on the line.

1. It seems like evry time the wind blows, a tree lim falls down.

_____

2. I tried to move it, but I scraped the pahm of my hand.

_____

3. I should have put on gloves befor I headed outside.

_____

4. Before long, I had cleared the whol yard.

_____

5. Now if only I new wher to put it all!

_____

© Weekly Reader Corp.

Monthly Review

Name _____

A. Find the mistakes. Write each sentence correctly on the line.

1. "Keri tell us about mysteries of outer space" said Mrs. Lampson.

   _____

2. Keri said "This book explains why scientists study comets and asteroids."

   _____

3. She continued "It has a table of contents, glossary, and index."

   _____

4. "The index gave the meanings of words that I didn't know" Keri said.

   _____

5. "I used the glossary to find the author's name" Keri stated.

   _____

B. Complete the crossword puzzle. Be careful! The answers are words that are commonly misspelled.

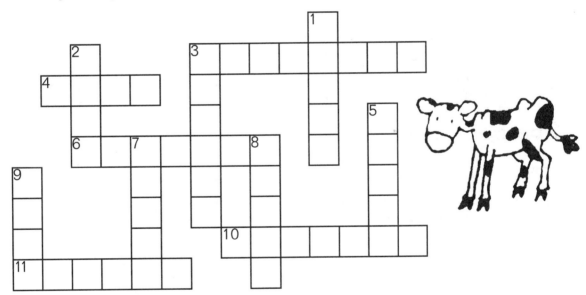

Across
3. Something that is special
4. They do; he _____
6. Think something is real
10. Fold in paper or skin
11. A scare

Down
1. Opposite of right
2. _____ and brush
3. A pal
5. Wait _____ I see you!
7. Opposite of cry
8. Each; all
9. Baby cow

Compound Sentences

Name _____

①

A compound sentence is made up of two complete sentences joined by a conjunction *(and, or, but, so, yet)*. *The weather was warm, so she went swimming.*

Decide whether the sentence is a compound sentence. Write *Yes* or *No* on the line.

_____ 1. Mrs. Krauss brought her rabbit to school, and I got to hold it.

_____ 2. It is white all over, so she named it Marshmallow.

_____ 3. Marshmallow has pink ears and a twitchy nose.

_____ 4. Kelly and I are in charge of feeding Marshmallow.

_____ 5. Marshmallow can hop fast, but it can't get out of our room.

Compound Sentences

Name _____

②

You can join two related sentences to form a compound sentence. Use a comma and a conjunction *(and, or, but, so, yet)* when you form a compound sentence. *The weather was warm. + She went swimming. = The weather was warm, so she went swimming.*

Choose the best conjunction to join the sentences. Write the word on the line.

1. Tanya skated fast, _____ she didn't win.
   (but, so)

2. Jim likes to race, _____ Pam does too.
   (or, and)

3. Kent hurt his ankle, _____ he couldn't jump.
   (so, or)

4. We can run on the track, _____ we can hike the trail.
   (so, or)

5. I love to run, _____ I'm running farther every day.
   (but, and)

DAILY LANGUAGE PRACTICE

Compound Sentences

③

Name _____

You can join two related sentences to form a compound sentence. Use a comma and a conjunction *(and, or, but, so, yet)* when you form a compound sentence. *The weather was warm. + She went swimming. = The weather was warm, so she went swimming.*

Is the compound sentence punctuated correctly? Write *Yes* or *No* on the line.

_____ 1. Wildfires break out and, the smoke jumpers are ready.

_____ 2. An alarm sounds at the base, and smoke jumpers grab their gear.

_____ 3. Airplanes take them to the fires and they jump out.

_____ 4. Their parachutes open, and they land near a fire.

_____ 5. It is a dangerous job, yet they continue to do it.

DAILY LANGUAGE PRACTICE

Compound Sentences

④

Name _____

You can join two related sentences to form a compound sentence. Use a comma and a conjunction *(and, or, but, so, yet)* when you form a compound sentence. *The weather was warm. + She went swimming. = The weather was warm, so she went swimming.*

Choose the best conjunction to join the sentences. Write the word on the line.

1. People have studied dinosaur fossils for years, _____ (or, but) now it is easier than before.

2. Scientists find fossil bones, _____ (and, or) then they figure out how to fit the bones together.

3. They enter the details into a computer, _____ (but, and) it creates a model of the dinosaur.

4. The computer model can show that scientists were right, _____ (so, or) it can prove them wrong.

5. Scientists once thought Apatasaurus held its neck high, _____ (but, and) a computer model showed that the neck was probably held low.

Compound Sentences

Name

You can join two related sentences to form a compound sentence. Use a comma and a conjunction *(and, or, but, so, yet)* when you form a compound sentence. *The weather was warm. + She went swimming. = The weather was warm, so she went swimming.*

Use a conjunction to join the two sentences. Write the compound sentence correctly on the line.

1. People used to be afraid of comets. Now we know they are not a sign of disaster.

   _____

2. Some comets have long bright tails. Others have only a faint tail.

   _____

3. Comets hold frozen gases. A dust like charcoal forms a crust over the outside.

   _____

4. Scientists collected dust from a comet. They can study it.

   _____

5. We have learned much about comets. There is still much that is unknown.

   _____

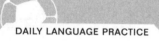

Compound Sentences

Name

Join the sentences. Write the compound sentence correctly on the line.

1. Life was different long ago. There are some things that are the same.

   _____

2. Children went to school. All ages were in the same classroom.

   _____

3. Children long ago had to do chores. Kids still do chores today.

   _____

4. Girls often helped their mothers sew. Boys helped their fathers in the fields.

   _____

5. Blocks were a popular toy. They are still popular today.

   _____

Run-On Sentences

(1)

Name _____

A run-on sentence includes two sentences that flow together. *The sky grew dark the rain began.*

Is it a run-on sentence? Write *Yes* or *No* on the line.

_____ 1. Animal teeth come in different shapes and sizes.

_____ 2. A tiger has sharp teeth they slice through food.

_____ 3. An elephant digs up food with its tusks and chews with its teeth.

_____ 4. A shark grabs food with its teeth they are sharp as razors.

_____ 5. A hippo crushes food it has powerful jaws.

Run-On Sentences

(2)

Name _____

A run-on sentence includes two sentences that flow together. *The sky grew dark the rain began.*

Correct each run-on sentence. Write two sentences on the line.

1. There are many types of weather rain is a type of weather.

_____

2. Snow is made of tiny pieces of ice they stick together to make snowflakes.

_____

3. Rain brings water to drink plants need water to grow.

_____

4. Wind is moving air it carries things from one place to another.

_____

5. Tornados are twisting winds they are often caused by thunderstorms.

_____

Run-On Sentences

Name

A run-on sentence includes two sentences
that flow together. *The sky grew dark the rain began.*

Is it a run-on sentence?
Write *Yes* or *No* on the line.

_____ 1. The White House is where the president lives in Washington, D.C.

_____ 2. The U.S. flag is an American symbol it is called "Old Glory."

_____ 3. Mount Rushmore is a national monument in South Dakota.

_____ 4. The Statue of Liberty is a symbol of freedom and friendship.

_____ 5. The bald eagle is our national bird it lives only in North America.

© Weekly Reader Corp.

Run-On Sentences

Name

A run-on sentence includes two sentences that flow together. *The sky grew dark the rain began.*

Correct each run-on sentence. Write two sentences on the line.

1. People use money every day what do you know about it?

_____

2. A dollar bill lasts almost two years then it needs to be shredded.

_____

3. U.S. bills are printed on paper the paper is made from linen and cotton.

_____

4. Each day the government prints 37 million bills they are worth about $696 million.

_____

5. About 18 tons (16 metric tons) of ink are used each day that is equal to the weight of three elephants!

© Weekly Reader Corp.

DAILY LANGUAGE PRACTICE

Run-On Sentences

Name _____

A run-on sentence includes two sentences that flow together. *The sky grew dark the rain began.*

Is it a run-on sentence? Write *Yes* or *No* on the line.

_____ 1. There are many helpful workers in your community.

_____ 2. Police officers help keep you safe they make sure people follow the law.

_____ 3. Construction workers build roads, bridges, and houses.

_____ 4. Doctors treat sick people and they help them stay healthy they know a lot.

_____ 5. Some firefighters are volunteers they don't get paid.

© Weekly Reader Corp.

DAILY LANGUAGE PRACTICE

Run-On Sentences

Name _____

Find the mistakes. Write each sentence correctly on the line.

1. Many kids play outside in the summer follow these simple rules to stay safe.

_____

2. Follow water-safety rules always swim with a buddy.

_____

3. Sun can burn your skin always remember to use sunscreen.

_____

4. Skating, biking, and riding a scooter are fun they help you stay fit.

_____

5. Always wear a helmet when you ride and skate stay away from busy streets.

_____

© Weekly Reader Corp.

Week Thirty-Five

Suffixes

Name _____

A suffix is a word ending. A suffix changes the meaning of a base word. The suffix *-er* means "someone who does." Add it to *think* to get *thinker*. *Thinker* means "someone who thinks."

Add the suffix *-er* to a word in the first sentence. Write the new word on the line.

1. My mom loves to garden. She is a _____.

2. My dad paints. He is a _____.

3. My sister climbs mountains. She is a mountain _____.

4. My brother plays football. He is a football _____.

5. My uncle trains dogs. He is a dog _____.

© Weekly Reader Corp.

Week Thirty-Five

Suffixes

Name _____

② (circled number)

A suffix is a word ending. A suffix changes the meaning of a base word. The suffix *-er* means "someone who does." If a word ends in *-e*, just add *-r*. *Dive + -r = diver.*

Add the suffix *-er* to each word. Write the new word on the line. Then write a sentence using each new word.

1. explore _____
_____

2. write _____
_____

3. drive _____
_____

4. dance _____
_____

5. move _____

© Weekly Reader Corp.

Suffixes

(3)

Name _____

A suffix is a word ending. A suffix changes the meaning of a base word. The suffix *–ful* means "full of" or "with." Add *–ful* to *hope* to get *hopeful*. *Hopeful* means "full of hope."

Add the suffix *–ful* to each word. Write the meaning of the new word on the line.

1. play   _____

   meaning: _____

2. help   _____

   meaning: _____

3. hope   _____

   meaning: _____

4. health   _____

   meaning: _____

5. color   _____

   meaning: _____

Suffixes

(4)

Name _____

A suffix is a word ending. A suffix changes the meaning of a base word. The suffix *–less* means "without." Add *–less* to *hope* to get *hopeless*. *Hopeless* means "without hope."

Add the prefix *–less* to each word. Write the meaning of the new word on the line.

1. meaning   _____

   meaning: _____

2. fear   _____

   meaning: _____

3. joy   _____

   meaning: _____

4. odor   _____

   meaning: _____

5. friend   _____

   meaning: _____

Suffixes

Name

A suffix is a word ending. A suffix changes the meaning of a base word. The suffix *–able* means "able to be." Add *–able* to *manage* to get *manageable*. *Manageable* means "able to be managed."

Circle each word with the suffix *–able*. Write the meaning of the word on the line.

1. We believed our old dog was trainable.

_____

2. The trainer, Keith, was a likable person.

_____

3. He was dependable too.

_____

4. He gave us many valuable tips.

_____

5. Our dog's progress was unbelievable!

_____

Suffixes

Name

Add a suffix from the box to each base word. (Use each suffix once.) Write the new word on the line. Then write a sentence using each new word.

> –less   –er   –able   –r   –ful

RAIL PASS
ONE FARE

1. chew _____

_____

2. read _____

_____

3. ticket _____

_____

4. fear _____

_____

5. bike _____

DAILY LANGUAGE PRACTICE

Usage Review

① 1

Name _____

Some words are commonly misused. Some of these are homophones such as *their*, *they're*, and *there*. *Their* shows that "they" own something. *They're* means "they are." *There* is a location.

Write the correct word on the line.

1. Maria and Carlos are planning _____ vacation.
   (there, their, they're)

2. _____ thinking about the Grand Canyon.
   (There, Their, They're)

3. Maria isn't sure she wants to go _____.
   (there, their, they're)

4. _____ going to have to make up _____ minds quickly!
   (There, Their, They're)   (there, their, they're)

5. Otherwise, _____ won't be time to get tickets.
   (there, their, they're)

© Weekly Reader Corp.

DAILY LANGUAGE PRACTICE

Usage Review

② 2

Name _____

Some words are commonly misused. You should not use two negative words (*no*, *not*, *never*, *none*, *nothing*, *neither*, etc.) together.

Is the sentence correct? Write *Yes* or *No* on the line.

_____ 1. The old lion would not eat nothing.

_____ 2. He doesn't have any teeth.

_____ 3. The zookeeper had never seen nothing like it.

_____ 4. He didn't know what to do.

_____ 5. No one else did neither.

© Weekly Reader Corp.

Usage Review

Name _____

③

Some words are commonly misused. Some of these are homophones. Others are words with similar spellings.

Write the correct word on the line.

1. What is the _____ like today?
   (whether, weather)

2. I will decide what to _____ when I know.
   (wear, where)

3. I choose _____ clothes when it is hot.
   (lose, loose)

4. I can see my _____ when it is cold.
   (breathe, breath)

5. I wonder _____ I'll be able to see it today?
   (whether, weather)

Usage Review

Name _____

④

Some words are commonly misused. Some of these are homophones such as *to*, *two*, and *too*. *To* shows movement toward a place. *Two* is the number. *Too* means "also."

These sentences have mistakes. Write the sentences correctly on the lines.

1. I am going too the zoo.

   _____

2. The zoo has to pandas.

   _____

3. Do you want to go to?

   _____

4. We have seen the pandas too times already.

   _____

5. Let's go two the museum instead.

   _____

Usage Review

Name _____

⑤

Some words are commonly misused. Some of these are homophones such as *its* and *it's* or *accept* and *except*. *Its* shows ownership, while *it's* means "it is." *Accept* means to receive something. *Except* means everything but that which is named.

Write the correct word on the line.

1. Our school is proud of _____ math team.
   (its, it's)

2. The team will _____ an award today.
   (accept, except)

3. I know everyone on the team _____ Pete.
   (accept, except)

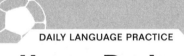

4. _____ time for the award.
   (its, it's)

5. I wonder where the team will keep _____ trophy.
   (its, it's)

Usage Review

Name _____

Find the mistakes. Write the sentence correctly on the line.

1. The engineer had never built nothing like it.

   _____

2. She wondered weather the children would like there playscape.

   _____

3. "Its to late too worry about that now," she thought.

   _____

4. She took a deep breathe.

   _____

5. Then she stepped forward to except everyone's thanks.

   _____

Monthly Review

Name _____

A. Find the mistakes. Write each sentence correctly on the line.

1. Bright lights are part of many winter holidays they look so pretty.

   _____

2. People carry candles in a parade for Las Posadas but I haven't never seen one.

   _____

3. Ramadan is an Islamic holiday, people carry there lanterns in the street.

   _____

4. People celebrate Christmas with lighted trees and they light candles
   for Hanukkah.

   _____

5. And, weather you no it or not, bright lights are part of Diwali and Kwanzaa to.

   _____

**B. Find five words with the suffixes *–er, –less, –ful, –able*. Look across and
down. Write the words and their meanings on the lines.**

```
E  N  J  O  Y  A  B  L  E
X  P  O  K  N  M  D  W  C
I  K  Y  W  E  D  U  S  Q
Y  P  F  R  Q  U  S  I  M
E  B  U  I  L  D  E  R  A
F  H  L  T  C  A  L  U  D
A  L  W  E  R  S  E  K  B
L  U  B  R  U  I  S  C  L
W  O  Z  E  M  B  S  T  T
```

_____ *meaning:* _____

_____ *meaning:* _____

_____ *meaning:* _____

_____ *meaning:* _____

meaning: _____

Daily Language Practice
Answers — Grade 3

Week 1
Day One
1. Yes 2. No 3. Yes 4. Yes 5. No
Day Two
1. Coral (reefs) are (home) to many (animals). 2. The (reefs) are found near the (surface) of some (oceans). 3. The (Great Barrier Reef) is near (Australia). 4. It is (home) to (jellyfish) and (octopuses). 5. (Sponges) and (sharks) also live there.
Day Three
1. Mexico 2. Mojave Desert 3. Chicago 4. Indian Ocean 5. Blue Ridge Mountains
Day Four
1. Our sun is a star. 2. Stars are made of hot gases. 3. Planets move around the sun. 4. Some scientists study planets and stars. 5. They use special tools like telescopes.
Day Five
1. Our country is the (United States of America). 2. (George Washington) was the first president. 3. (Alaska) is the largest state. 4. The (Rocky Mountains) are in the West. 5. The (Mississippi River) is a long river.
Review
1. The (Pilgrims) sailed from (England) in 1620. 2. Their boat was called the (Mayflower). 3. They landed near (Plymouth Rock) and built a fort. 4. (Squanto) was a friend to the (Pilgrims). 5. He taught them to hunt deer, plant corn, and find berries.

Week 2
Day One
1. E 2. S 3. Q 4. Q 5. S
Day Two
1. Q 2. S 3. S 4. Q 5. E
Day Three
1. ? 2. . 3. ? 4. . 5. !
Day Four
1. Have you ever looked at the night sky? 2. What a lot of stars! 3. They are part of our galaxy. 4. Do you know what a galaxy is? 5. A galaxy is an island of stars.
Day Five
1. ! 2. . 3. ? 4. . 5. ?
Review
1. Do you take care of your lungs? 2. Exercise makes your lungs strong. 3. Doctors make sure your lungs are healthy. 4. Did you know that smoking can harm your lungs? 5. You should never smoke!

Week 3
Day One
1. amphibian 2. animal 3. bird 4. fish 5. mammal 6. reptile
Day Two
1. Yes 2. No 3. No 4. Yes 5. No
Day Three
1. other 2. onion 3. onward 4. ounce 5. ostrich
Day Four
1. ankle 2. arm 3. elbow 4. face 5. foot
Day Five
1. cobweb 2. castle 3. cattle 4. coin 5. catnip
Review
1. Africa, America, Antarctica, Asia
2. calf, cub, duckling, piglet
3. daisy, lily, rose, zinnia
4. pad, paper, pen, pencil
5. raven, robin, rooster, sparrow

Week 4
Day One
1. raise 2. neighbor 3. trail 4. crayon 5. weigh
Day Two
1. video 2. busy 3. any 4. thief 5. idea
Day Three
1. my 2. sight 3. fly 4. lie 5. find
Day Four
1. most 2. coach 3. ago 4. spoke 5. gold
Day Five
1. goose 2. crew 3. juice 4. broom 5. soup
Review
1. The island's warm breezes blew gently through the trees. 2. I waved hello to my friends as I walked past. 3. Fresh fruit was piled high in the market. 4. I picked out mangos and gave them to the woman to weigh. 5. Then I added them to my load.

Month 1 Review
A. 1. Did you know that chimps live in family groups? 2. Mother chimps carry their babies on their backs. 3. They make nests each night. 4. They build them high in the trees. 5. The nests are made of leaves.
B. cobweb, coin, complete, condition
What can you catch but not throw?
A cold.
C. Common Nouns: school, friend, car, street
Proper nouns will vary.

Week 5
Day One
1. No 2. Yes 3. No 4. Yes 5. Yes
Day Two
1. Dr. Jane Goodall (studied) chimpanzees. 2. She (lived) with them in Africa. 3. Dr. Goodall (learned) a lot about the chimps. 4. Chimpanzees often (stay) in large groups. 5. They (use) tools to (gather) food.
Day Three
1. float 2. protect 3. spill 4. suggest 5. improve
Day Four
1. Some holidays (make) winter bright. 2. Many African Americans (celebrate) Kwanzaa. 3. Some people (decorate) trees for Christmas. 4. Jewish people (observe) Hanukkah for eight nights. 5. Some families (eat) special foods at the end of Ramadan.
Day Five
Answers will vary.
Review
1. Bald eagles (live) in almost every state in America. 2. They (lay) eggs from November to January. 3. The eggs (hatch) after 35 days. 4. The young eagles (fly) about three months later. 5. Thousands of eagles (gather) in Alaska to (catch) salmon.

Week 6
Day One
1. Davis Elementary School 2. Grand Canyon 3. Running Fox Trail 4. Mount Hood 5. Alexander Graham Bell
Day Two
1. The Rocky Mountains are in the United States. 2. They stretch from New Mexico to Canada. 3. Many people visit Pikes Peak. 4. It was named for Zebulon Pike. 5. The first woman to climb the mountain was Julia Holmes.
Day Three
1. New York City 2. Lake Superior 3. Pacific Ocean 4. Golden Gate Bridge 5. Colorado River
Day Four
1. George Washington Carver was a great American. 2. He was born near Diamond Grove, Missouri. 3. The George Washington Carver National Monument honors his memory. 4. Later, Carver taught at the Tuskegee Institute. 5. He invented peanut butter while he was working in Alabama.

Day Five
1. Mojave Desert 2. Death Valley
3. America 4. July 5. Chloride City
Review
1. The ocean didn't scare Amelia Earhart. 2. She flew across the Atlantic Ocean by herself. 3. She also flew from Honolulu to California. 4. In 1937, Earhart started to fly around the world. 5. Her plane disappeared near Howland Island in the Pacific Ocean.

Week 7
Day One
1. stars 2. states 3. stripes
4. stickers 5. words
Day Two
1. foxes 2. beaches 3. classes
4. brushes 5. inches
Day Three
1. centuries 2. opportunities
3. territories 4. communities 5. cities
Day Four
1. teeth 2. men 3. geese
4. children 5. women
Day Five
1. benches 2. robins 3. cherries
4. feet 5. butterflies
Review
1. Libraries are like treasure chests. 2. They have books that are full of adventures. 3. Climb the world's tallest mountains with Reinhold Messner. 4. Push your way through the branches and vines of the Amazon. 5. What riches will you find in your library?

Week 8
Day One
1. Yes 2. No 3. Yes 4. Yes 5. No
Day Two
1. d 2. e 3. b 4. a 5. c
Day Three
1. author – writer 2. calm – peaceful
3. correct – right 4. glance – look
5. smell – odor
Day Four
1. visitor 2. pleasant 3. task
4. hollow 5. observe
Day Five
1. terrified – scared
2. gloom – darkness
3. begin – start 4. autumn – fall
5. brave – heroic
Review
1. huge 2. tiny 3. frightening
4. speedy 5. noisy

Month 2 Review
A. 1. Some early Americans led exciting lives. 2. Paul Revere rode to Lexington, Massachusetts, at midnight. 3. The British soldiers were on their way to arrest Samuel Adams. 4. Paul Revere warned everyone along the way. 5. Soon, the Minutemen were ready to fight for freedom.
B. bring, lift, march, race, scratch

C.

Crossword puzzle solution:
- 3 Across: STRONG
- 4 Across: UNHAPPY
- 6 Across: LOOK
- 7 Across: YELL
- 1 Down: FUD(S)
- 2 Down: TINY
- 5 Down: PULLS

Week 9
Day One
1. June 2, 1933
2. December 5, 1957
3. March 22, 2006
4. September 23, 1999
5. April 12, 2001
Day Two
1. Denver, Colorado
2. Atlanta, Georgia
3. Topeka, Kansas
4. Hartford, Connecticut
5. Madison, Wisconsin
Day Three
1. Abraham Lincoln was born February 12, 1809. 2. He was born in Hodgenville, Kentucky. 3. Lincoln moved to New Salem, Illinois. 4. He was elected president on November 6, 1860. 5. President Lincoln freed the slaves in the South on January 1, 1863.
Day Four
1. The world's largest watermelon was grown in Hope, Arkansas. 2. It weighed almost 270 pounds (123 kg) on September 3, 2005. 3. The world's heaviest tomato grew in Edmond, Oklahoma. 4. A 19-pound (9 kg) carrot was grown in Palmer, Alaska. 5. The biggest pumpkin came from North Cambria, Pennsylvania.
Day Five
1. No 2. Yes 3. Yes 4. No 5. Yes
Review
1. George Washington was born on February 22, 1732. 2. The White House is in Washington, D.C. 3. Mount Rushmore is near Keystone, South Dakota. 4. Paul Revere lived in Boston, Massachusetts. 5. The American flag was introduced on June 14, 1777.

Week 10
Day One
1. speaking 2. baking 3. fixing
4. sliding 5. walking
Day Two
1. digging 2. swimming 3. flapping
4. setting 5. stopping
Day Three
1. avoided 2. crashed 3. enjoyed
4. collected 5. reminded
Day Four
1. lived 2. ruled 3. died
4. removed 5. provided
Day Five
1. supplied 2. chopped 3. hurried
4. robbed 5. buried

Review
1. Drew was bullied by an older student. 2. The bully teased Drew and called him names. 3. Sometimes bullying can involve hitting or pushing too. 4. Drew helped pass a new law in Maine. 5. Schools changed their rules about how they are handling bullies.

Week 11
Day One
1. A koala (doesn't) eat just anything.
2. (It'll) only eat eucalyptus leaves.
3. And that (isn't) all. 4. It (won't) eat leaves from some eucalyptus trees.
5. (They're) very picky eaters!
Day Two
1. doesn't 2. we've 3. he's
4. wasn't 5. she'll
Day Three
1. did not 2. you will 3. she is
4. here is 5. I am
Day Four
1. aren't 2. They're 3. It's
4. don't 5. wouldn't
Day Five
1. We haven't started our project yet. 2. Lynn said she'd write the report. 3. I'll illustrate it. 4. You've got to present it to the class. 5. Tyler won't be at school that day.
Review
1. What's Mount Rushmore? 2. It's a rock that has the faces of four presidents carved in it. 3. The faces on Mount Rushmore hadn't been cleaned in years. 4. Cleaning the faces wasn't an easy job. 5. Now, they're squeaky-clean!

Week 12
Day One
1. drink 2. score 3. scarf
4. scared 5. blast
Day Two
1. smash 2. think 3. blink
4. crumble 5. flash
Day Three
1. grand 2. plenty 3. scrub
4. string 5. sprinkle
Day Four
1. behind 2. dream 3. gift
4. trunk 5. young
Day Five
1. ring 2. belong 3. dragon
4. thump 5. parent
Review
1. The teacher showed the class how to make screen prints. 2. One student made a blue print. 3. Another used green ink. 4. One girl decided to paint her picture. 5. Someone else used a stamp.

Month 3 Review
A. 1. May 10, 1869, was a grand day! 2. At Promontory, Utah, the last spike joined two American railroads. 3. Workers began building the Central Pacific railroad in California on October 26, 1863.

4. About a month later, the Union Pacific broke ground in Omaha, Nebraska. 5. People across America celebrated the quick new way of travel.
B. 1. hurrying 2. located 3. buries 4. libraries 5. flying
Sentences will vary.
C. Answers will vary.

Week 13
Day One
1. Yes 2. No 3. Yes 4. Yes 5. No
Day Two
1. Ben reads about snakes, alligators, and crocodiles. 2. Iris reads about stars, planets, and moons. 3. Carlos studies rocks, leaves, and insects. 4. Riley collects shells, feathers, and seeds. 5. Ben, Iris, Carlos, and Riley like science.
Day Three
1. No; California, Nevada, and Idaho often have wildfires. 2. Yes 3. Yes 4. No; Dry(,) grass, leaves, and trees catch fire quickly. 5. No; Smoke jumpers take tools, food, and water(,) with them.
Day Four
1. Oaks, maples, and elms have green leaves in the summer. 2. Their leaves turn yellow, red, and orange in the fall. 3. The roots, trunks, and branches of the trees can live through winter. 4. Spring sunshine warms the air, ground, and trees. 5. Leaves use sunlight, water, and air to make food for the trees.
Day Five
1. Yes 2. No 3. No 4. Yes 5. No
Review
1. Hurricanes, tornados, and blizzards are big storms. 2. These storms can bring wind, rain, or snow. 3. People need to have food, water, and flashlights ready. 4. Sometimes people stay at a school, hotel, or other safe place. 5. Roads, homes, and buildings may need to be fixed.

Week 14
Day One
1. bellow 2. guards 3. stays 4. carry 5. eats
Day Two
1. are 2. know 3. is 4. live 5. has
Day Three
1. Rain falls from clouds.
2. Too much rain causes floods.
3. Lightning storms are dangerous.
4. A blizzard is a big snowstorm.
5. Radar helps predict the weather.
Day Four
1. are 2. nibble 3. makes 4. stores 5. dig
Day Five
1. are 2. belong 3. lives 4. is 5. face

Review
1. The U.S. Treasury makes our paper money. 2. A government bank stores the bills in a vault where they will be safe. 3. Trained guards deliver the bills to local banks. 4. People spend the money in stores. 5. The government shreds the bills when they are worn out.

Week 15
Day One
1. O 2. F 3. F 4. O 5. F
Day Two
Answers will vary.
Day Three
1. F 2. F 3. O 4. F 5. O
Day Four
1. O 2. F 3. O 4. F 5. F
Day Five
1. F 2. F 3. F 4. O 5. O
Review
1. O 2. F 3. F 4. F 5. O

Week 16
Day One
1. Yes 2. Yes 3. No 4. No 5. Yes
Day Two
1. c 2. d 3. e 4. a 5. b
Day Three
1. friend 2. take 3. crooked 4. loose 5. shallow
Day Four
Answers will vary.
Day Five
1. cold 2. fastest 3. wider 4. dangerous 5. Thin
Review
1. The gym was (noisy) when the game started, but it soon grew (quiet). 2. If I can't (find) my notebook, I'll (lose) the results of my experiment. 3. I wanted to get to class (early), but now I'm running (late). 4. Do you like to (lead) or (follow) when you go hiking? 5. We all looked (clumsy) next to the (graceful) dancer.

Month 4 Review
A. 1. My favorite subjects are math, science, and reading. 2. I am always checking out books from the library. 3. Last week I picked out books about spiders, comets, and dinosaurs. 4. The librarian likes to see me reading so many books.
5. Tomorrow I may surprise her and check out a mystery!
B. best, worst; buy, sell; early, late; loud, quiet
C. Answers will vary.

Week 17
Day One
1. No 2. Yes 3. No 4. Yes 5. Yes
Day Two
1. cuddly 2. sharp 3. twirling 4. bouncy 5. funny

Day Three
1. Mexico's Volcano of Fire is an (active) volcano. 2. It has been shooting (hot) gas into the sky. 3. Scientists have noticed a pattern in (recent) activity. 4. They expect an (explosive) eruption in the next 10 years. 5. Scientists are using (special) tools to watch the volcano.
Day Four
1. unusual 2. clever 3. wild 4. rainy 5. busy
Day Five
1. Madagascar is a (large) (tropical) island near Africa. 2. (Many) (rare) animals live in its (disappearing) forests. 3. Scientists just discovered the (tiny), (wide-eyed) mouse lemur. 4. It has a (white) stripe on its nose and (short), (rounded) ears. 5. It has (orange), (maroon), and (white) fur.
Review
1. giant, bamboo 2. cool, high 3. Thick, woolly 4. strong, tough 5. black, white

Week 18
Day One
1. sang 2. dug 3. blew 4. drew 5. rode
Day Two
1. let 2. hit 3. burst 4. shut 5. quit
Day Three
1. bent 2. felt 3. spent 4. lost 5. crept
Day Four
1. broke 2. find 3. ate 4. understood 5. fly
Day Five
1. led 2. chose 3. shot 4. slid 5. bled
Review
1. Martin Luther King Jr. went to Washington, D.C. 2. On the steps of the Lincoln Memorial, he made a speech. 3. He spoke out for equal rights. 4. Dr. King said that people should be treated fairly. 5. He taught us that one person can make a difference.

Week 19
Day One
1. c 2. d 3. a 4. e 5. b
Day Two
1. a jellyfish's tentacles 2. a clam's shell 3. a shark's fin 4. the diver's mask 5. the boat's engine
Day Three
1. children's 2. elephant's 3. snake's 4. camel's 5. ostrich's
Day Four
1. tree's leaves 2. squirrel's cheeks 3. bear's den 4. geese's cries 5. Winter's snow
Day Five
1. singular 2. plural 3. plural 4. singular 5. plural

Review
1. The day's hike was over, and now it was time to rest. 2. The campers' happy shouts echoed across the hillside. 3. The campfire's smoke rose through the air. 4. The girls' songs welcomed the stars. 5. Soon the night's quiet darkness fell over the camp.

Week 20
Day One
1. friends 2. valentines 3. mailboxes
4. inches 5. crackers
Day Two
1. flies 2. pennies 3. ladies
4. parties 5. daisies
Day Three
Sentences will vary.
1. hoped 2. smiled 3. divided
4. saved 5. moved
Day Four
1. blankets 2. supplies 3. pairs
4. companies 5. addresses
Day Five
1. crying 2. shaking 3. escaping
4. hurrying 5. blaming
Review
1. Sloths live in the jungles of South America. 2. They are the slowest-moving mammals in the world.
3. They spend most of their time hanging upside down from branches.
4. Colonies of green algae grow on their fur. 5. Harpy eagles are natural enemies of the sloth.

Month 5 Review
A. 1. My friend's voice is beautiful.
2. She sang at the school's concert last night. 3. The crowd grew quiet, listening. 4. When the song ended, the crowd's applause thundered through the room. 5. Sarah's back straightened with pride as she moved off the stage.
B.

```
                              ²R
                ²S L E E K
                              C
  ³T           ⁴C L E V E R
  H                           N
  ⁵I N D E ⁶P E N D E N T
  C           O           R
  K           ⁸P L E A S A N T
              U           R
        ⁹S I L E N T
              A
        ¹⁰F A R A W A Y
```

Week 21
Day One
1. Yes 2. No 3. Yes 4. No 5. Yes
Day Two
1. gently 2. often 3. correctly
4. there 5. bravely
Day Three
1. Amazingly 2. usually 3. carefully
4. Sometimes 5. regularly

Day Four
1. safely 2. rudely 3. warmly
4. foolishly 5. brightly
Day Five
Sentences will vary.
1. happily 2. busily 3. speedily
4. hungrily 5. angrily
Review
1. soundly 2. Suddenly 3. shortly
4. uncontrollably 5. Finally

Week 22
Day One
1. P 2. S 3. P 4. P 5. S
Day Two
1. (Danny Way) leaped over the Great Wall of China on a skateboard.
2. (He) used a ramp that he brought from California. 3. (Danny) was going nearly 50 miles per hour over the wall.
4. (Parts of the Great Wall) are more than 2,000 years old. 5. (The wall) is about 4,000 miles long.
Day Three
1. No 2. Yes 3. Yes 4. Yes 5. No
Day Four
Answers will vary.
Day Five
1. On August 29, Hurricane Katrina hit the Gulf Coast. 2. The fierce storm destroyed buildings, homes, and trees.
3. After Katrina passed, most of New Orleans, Louisiana, was flooded.
4. Cleanup after Katrina is expected to take months or even years. 5. People across America have reached out to people hurt by Katrina.
Review
1. With a wave of his wand, Harry Potter has put kids under his spell.
2. Millions of kids lined up to buy the sixth book in the series. 3. Kids today are going wild for books about magical worlds. 4. Many of the books are being turned into movies. 5. Do you think that the books are casting a spell on people?

Week 23
Day One
1. We 2. He 3. They 4. I 5. She
Day Two
1. He 2. She 3. They 4. We 5. It
Day Three
1. Kate and I planted seeds in the garden. 2. Tim and I watered the seeds.
3. Kate and I pulled the weeds. 4. Tim and I dug up the carrots. 5. Kate, Tim, and I washed and ate the carrots.
Day Four
1. it 2. her 3. us 4. him 5. them
Day Five
1. you 2. it 3. him 4. them 5. her
Review
1. My friends and I have some tiny silkworm eggs. 2. It is hard to see them. 3. They hatched into little caterpillars. 4. We fed the caterpillars mulberry leaves. 5. Then we watched one as it made a cocoon.

Week 24
Day One
1. cold 2. larger 3. heavier
4. thick 5. longer
Day Two
1. tallest 2. longest 3. largest
4. smallest 5. fastest
Day Three
1. more 2. better 3. less
4. best 5. least
Day Four
1. safer, safest 2. later, latest
3. nicer, nicest 4. gentler, gentlest
5. simpler, simplest
Day Five
1. itchier 2. craziest 3. rainier
4. trickiest 5. laziest
Review
1. Taiwan is an island near China. It is smaller than Japan. 2. The island is about 90 miles (145 km) at its widest point. 3. The mountains are the rainiest part of the island. 4. The world's tallest building is in Taiwan.
5. Some people think that Taiwanese opera is better than the movies.

Month 6 Review
A. 1. Much of the continent of Africa is a grassland. 2. Mr. Richards says it is home to many different animals.
3. He told us that giraffes are the tallest animals in the world. 4. Once, Mr. Richards saw them running across the plains. 5. Lions live in a pride. They live in Africa too.
B. Answers will vary.
C. tiniest, bigger, bouncier, older, muddiest
Sentences will vary.

Week 25
Day One
1. unlock; opposite of lock
2. uncover; opposite of cover
3. unhealthy; not healthy
4. uncomfortable; not comfortable
5. unknown; not known
Day Two
1. redo 2. refill 3. retake
4. reglue 5. retrace
Sentences will vary.
Day Three
1. impolite; not polite
2. improper; not proper
3. inactive; not active
4. incomplete; not complete
5. impatient; not patient
Day Four
1. disagree 2. disappear
3. disapprove 4. dishonest
5. discomfort
Sentences will vary.
Day Five
1. two 2. 100 3. three
4. eight 5. five

Review
1. The report was full of facts that were unimportant. 2. The students had to rewrite the report. 3. They were displeased. 4. They thought the task was impossible. 5. They finally restarted.

Week 26
Day One
1. Yes 2. No 3. Yes 4. No 5. Yes
Day Two
1. "Let's help with the coastal cleanup this year," suggested Maddie.
2. "That's a great idea!" Dad replied.
3. "Last year volunteers picked up lots of trash," Matt added. 4. "That trash can kill birds and other animals," Mom said. 4. "I'll get our gloves and trash bags!" Maddie exclaimed.
Day Three
1. No 2. No 3. Yes 4. No 5. Yes
Day Four
1. "Did you know that we are studying penguins?" Cooper asked his father. 2. "What have you learned?" Dad replied. 3. "Four types of penguins live on Antarctica," Cooper said. 4. "Early explorers thought they were fish!" he laughed. 5. "They are good swimmers," his father agreed.
Day Five
1. Yes 2. No 3. Yes 4. No 5. No
Review
1. "We went to Mesa Verde on vacation this summer," Lynn said. 2. "What's that?" I asked. 3. "It is the home of the Anasazi Indians," she replied. 4. "They lived thousands of years ago in cliff dwellings," continued Lynn. 5. "You can still see their houses today!" she exclaimed.

Week 27
Day One
1. ant 2. too or to 3. our 4. meet 5. ate
Day Two
1. know 2. read 3. deer 4. dew 5. sew
Day Three
1. blew 2. board 3. eight 4. won 5. hoarse
Day Four
1. night 2. knows 3. weak 4. pair or pare 5. tide
Day Five
1. through 2. deer 3. cheep 4. flew 5. bear
Review
1. How would you rather travel? 2. Some people like to drive cars. 3. Others like to sail their boats. 4. Riding in a train gives you time to read a book. 5. I prefer to fly in a plane.

Week 28
Day One
1. maple 2. eight 3. three 4. 16

Day Two
1. 10 feet 2. female Asian elephant 3. two tons 4. male African elephant
Day Three
1. Pacific Ocean 2. Indian Ocean 3. Puerto Rico Trench; Mariana Trench 4. Arctic Basin
Day Four
1. Nile 2. 3,800–4,000 miles 3. Africa 4. Yangtze
Day Five
1. eight 2. insects 3. no 4. spiders
Review
1. 37 minutes 2. Mars 3. Earth 4. 322 days

Month 7 Review
A. "Please read your story aloud," said Mr. Kent. 2. I started to groan, but then I got to my feet. 3. "The Boy Who Ate Eight Beets," I began. 4. I heard laughter break out around the room. 5. I grinned, then I read the rest of the story.
B. 1. Ivan, Charley, and Andrew 2. three 3. 12 years

Week 29
Day One
1. "I have swim practice after school," said Samantha. 2. "My first swim meet is this weekend," she continued. 3. "I like to swim too," said Kelsey. 4. "It's my favorite part of the summer," she said. 5. "Come swim with me," invited Samantha.
Day Two
1. Ben yelled, "Come look at this gila monster!" 2. Carmen said, "I can't believe that it can eat a bird." 3. Ben said, "Look. It says they're poisonous." 4. Carmen said, "I'm glad they're behind the glass." 5. Ben said, "Me, too!"
Day Three
1. "Remember that your reports are due tomorrow," said the teacher. 2. Mike said, "I'm almost finished." 3. "I have my notes and outline," he said. 4. "I've written my first draft," he went on. 5. Mike declared, "All I have to do is check it carefully tonight."
Day Four
1. Julia, where is your backpack? 2. Do you have your homework done, Kim? 3. Nico, this is a well-written story! 4. Katherine, let's ride bikes. 5. I'd rather go to the park, Lauren.
Day Five
1. "Are you going to play soccer this spring, Todd?" asked Dan. 2. Todd replied, "I sure am, Dan!" 3. "How about you, Brian?" Todd asked. 4. "Sure! Let's keep the team together, Todd," answered Brian. 5. Todd asked, "Do you have time for a game now, Dan?"
Review
1. "It snowed last night," Miguel said. 2. "Rosa, wake up!" he shouted.

3. Rosa asked, "What's all the shouting about?" 4. Miguel answered, "Look out the window at the snow!" 5. "Let's build a snowman, Miguel," suggested Rosa.

Week 30
Day One
1. No 2. No 3. Yes 4. Yes 5. No
Day Two
1. Monsters, Inc. 2. Beauty and the Beast 3. Remember the Titans 4. Back to the Future 5. Lady and the Tramp
Day Three
1. Yes 2. No 3. Yes 4. No 5. No
Day Four
1. Mr. Popper's Penguins made me laugh when I read it. 2. Sue liked the movie James and the Giant Peach. 3. We read The Sign of the Beaver in class. 4. Have you seen Jason and the Argonauts? 5. My family went to see The King and I.
Day Five
1. My little sister sings "I'm a Little Teapot." 2. "Over in the Meadow" is a counting poem. 3. "Home on the Range" is an old cowboy song. 4. We memorized Langston Hughes' poem "April Rain Song." 5. "Down by the Bay" is one of the silliest songs I know.
Review
1. One of my favorite books is Mrs. Frisby and the Rats of NIMH. 2. "Eletelephony" is a funny poem! 3. We sang "You Are My Sunshine" in our program. 4. Have you read My Life in Dog Years by Gary Paulsen? 5. Swiss Family Robinson was a great movie.

Week 31
Day One
1. Lynne Reid Banks 2. Charlott Web 3. No 4. Charlotte's Web 5. Brock Cole
Day Two
1. spiders 2. Chapter 1 3. the spider's life cycle 4. pages 14–1 5. Chapter 2
Day Three
1. a baby spider 2. egg sac 3. a animal that hunts or eats another 4. spinnerets 5. the rear part of spider's body
Day Four
1. 9 2. three (12, 13, and 14) 3. 8 4. 7 and 10 5. silk and spinneret
Day Five
1. spider 2. recluse spiders 3. predator 4. fishing spiders 5. eyes
Review
1. c 2. a 3. d 4. b 5. d

Week 32
Day One
1. special 2. sugar 3. again 4. animal 5. height

Day Two
1. chocolate 2. could 3. friend
4. wrinkle 5. always
Day Three
1. castles 2. knights 3. through
4. picture 5. interesting
Day Four
1. breakfast 2. until 3. wrap
4. listen 5. laugh
Day Five
1. Daylight 2. frightened 3. sure
4. knock 5. almost
Review
1. It seems like every time the wind blows, a tree limb falls down.
2. I tried to move it, but I scraped the palm of my hand. 3. I should have put on gloves before I headed outside.
4. Before long, I had cleared the whole yard. 5. Now if only I knew where to put it all!

Month 8 Review
A. 1. "Keri, tell us about <u>Mysteries of Outer Space</u>," said Mrs. Lampson.
2. Keri said, "This book explains why scientists study comets and asteroids." 3. She continued, "It has a table of contents, glossary, and index."
4. "The glossary gave the meanings of words that I didn't know," Keri said.
5. "I used the title page to find the author's name," Keri stated.
B.

Week 33
Day One
1. Yes 2. Yes 3. No 4. No 5. Yes
Day Two
1. but 2. and 3. so 4. or 5. and
Day Three
1. No 2. Yes 3. No 4. Yes 5. Yes
Day Four
1. but 2. and 3. and 4. or 5. but
Day Five
Conjunctions may vary.
1. People used to be afraid of comets, but now we know they are not a sign of disaster. 2. Some comets have long bright tails, but others have only a faint tail.
3. Comets hold frozen gases, and a dust like charcoal forms a crust over the outside. 4. Scientists collected dust from a comet, so they can study it. 5. We have learned much about comets, yet there is still much that is unknown.

Review
Conjunctions may vary.
1. Life was different long ago, yet there are some things that are the same. 2. Children went to school, but all ages were in the same classroom.
3. Children long ago had to do chores, and kids still do chores today.
4. Girls often helped their mothers sew, but boys helped their fathers in the fields. 5. Blocks were a popular toy, and they are still popular today.

Week 34
Day One
1. No 2. Yes 3. No 4. Yes 5. Yes
Day Two
1. There are many types of weather. Rain is a type of weather. 2. Snow is made of tiny pieces of ice. They stick together to make snowflakes.
3. Rain brings water to drink. Plants need water to grow. 4. Wind is moving air. It carries things from one place to another. 5. Tornados are twisting winds. They are often caused by thunderstorms.
Day Three
1. No 2. Yes 3. No 4. No 5. Yes
Day Four
1. People use money every day. What do you know about it? 2. A dollar bill lasts almost two years. Then it needs to be shredded. 3. U.S. bills are printed on paper. The paper is made from linen and cotton. 4. Each day the government prints 37 million bills. They are worth about $696 million. 5. About 18 tons (16 metric tons) of ink are used each day. That is equal to the weight of three elephants!
Day Five
1. No 2. Yes 3. No 4. Yes 5. Yes
Review
1. Many kids play outside in the summer. Follow these simple rules to stay safe. 2. Follow water-safety rules. Always swim with a buddy.
3. Sun can burn your skin. Always remember to use sunscreen.
4. Skating, biking, and riding a scooter are fun. They help you stay fit.
5. Always wear a helmet when you ride and skate. Stay away from busy streets.

Week 35
Day One
1. gardener 2. painter 3. climber
4. player 5. trainer
Day Two
1. explorer 2. writer 3. driver
4. dancer 5. mover
Sentences will vary.
Day Three
1. playful; full of play 2. helpful; full of help 3. hopeful; full of hope
4. healthful; full of health 5. colorful; full of color

Day Four
1. meaningless; without meaning
2. fearless; without fear 3. joyless; without joy 4. odorless; without odor
5. friendless; without a friend
Day Five
1. trainable; able to be trained
2. likable; able to be liked
3. dependable; able to be depended upon 4. valuable; able to be valued
5. unbelievable; not able to be believed
Review
1. chewable 2. reader 3. ticketless
4. fearful 5. biker
Sentences will vary.

Week 36
Day One
1. their 2. They're 3. there
4. They're; their 5. there
Day Two
1. No 2. Yes 3. No 4. Yes 5. No
Day Three
1. weather 2. wear 3. loose
4. breath 5. whether
Day Four
1. I am going to the zoo. 2. The zoo has two pandas. 3. Do you want to go too? 4. We have seen the pandas two times already. 5. Let's go to the museum instead.
Day Five
1. its 2. accept 3. except 4. It's
5. its
Review
1. The engineer had never built anything like it. 2. She wondered whether the children would like their playscape.
3. "It's too late to worry about that now," she thought. 4. She took a deep breath. 5. Then she stepped forward to accept everyone's thanks.

Month 9 Review
A. 1. Bright lights are part of many winter holidays. They look so pretty.
2. People carry candles in a parade for Las Posadas, but I haven't ever seen one. 3. Ramadan is an Islamic holiday. People carry their lanterns in the street. 4. People celebrate Christmas with lighted trees, and they light candles for Hanukkah.
5. And, whether you know it or not, bright lights are part of Diwali and Kwanzaa too.
B. builder – a person who builds
writer – a person who writes
joyful – full of joy
useless – without use
enjoyable – able to be enjoyed